Development of Cerebral Function in the Dog

ENGLAND: BUTTERWORTH & CO. (PUBLISHERS) LTD.
                LONDON: 88 Kingsway, W.C.2

AFRICA: BUTTERWORTH & CO. (AFRICA) LTD.
                DURBAN: 33/35 Beach Grove

AUSTRALIA: BUTTERWORTH & CO. (AUSTRALIA) LTD.
                SYDNEY: 6-8 O'Connell Street
                MELBOURNE: 473 Bourke Street
                BRISBANE: 240 Queen Street

CANADA: BUTTERWORTH & CO. (CANADA) LTD.
                TORONTO: 1367 Danforth Avenue, 6

NEW ZEALAND: BUTTERWORTH & CO. (NEW ZEALAND) LTD.
                WELLINGTON: 49/51 Ballance Street
                AUCKLAND: 35 High Street

U.S.A.:   BUTTERWORTH INC.
                WASHINGTON, D.C.: 7235 Wisconsin Avenue, 14

Development of Cerebral Function in the Dog

G. Pampiglione, M.D., M.R.C.P.

Physician in Charge, Department of EEG and Clinical Neurophysiology, The Hospital for Sick Children and Institute of Child Health (University of London); and from the Human Nutrition Research Unit (Medical Research Council)

LONDON

BUTTERWORTHS

1963

PRINTED IN GREAT BRITAIN BY HEADLEY BROTHERS LTD
109 KINGSWAY LONDON W C 2 AND ASHFORD KENT

Foreword

The use of the electroencephalogram as an aid to diagnosis has led to a great accumulation of records from human patients with brain disorders, but we still know very little about the cerebral activities which are expressed in the tracings. Dr Pampiglione's monograph adds fresh information from a different kind of brain. He has followed the changes which take place in the electro-encephalogram of the newborn puppy from the first two weeks, when its eyes are shut, until the third month, when it is fully weaned and will soon be able to lead the life of an adult dog. At each stage in development he has recorded the effects of sensory stimuli, barbiturates, etc., giving a concise account of the individual differences which are found, and he has added some records to illustrate abnormal features.

The most striking change occurs about eight weeks after birth, when the myelinization of the brain is advancing, for, at that stage, the records show a succession of large potential waves at a frequency of 4–6 cycles per second. After the third month, the oscillations have become much smaller and the dominant frequency has risen to 6–8 cycles per second.

His careful survey raises many points of great interest, and shows how much we may learn from comparative studies of this kind. It will be a guide of great value to future research on the electroencephalogram and on the changes which take place in the brain as it grows to maturity.

ADRIAN

London
   September 1963

Contents

Introduction

The study of the electrical activity of large groups of cells, and in particular of the brain of mammals, has been somewhat neglected by physiologists in recent years. Investigations of what appear to be simple neuronal systems have attracted neurophysiologists, while behavioural studies have multiplied. Few people have been concerned with the 'no-man's land' in between. Moreover, in experimental work on the central nervous system of mammals, greater attention has been devoted to the modes of action of fully developed systems rather than to the understanding of the ways in which those particular modes of action came to be established. It seems that in comparative neurophysiology the large volume of analytical work has overwhelmed our effort to understand and to integrate our fragmentary knowledge into a general system of life and growth of cerebral function.

The reader who hopes to find a comprehensive survey of developmental neurophysiology in this booklet will be disappointed, as it falls into the 'no-man's land' which has been mentioned above. It has been prepared for the beginner in electroencephalography (EEG) with an interest in the growth and development of the brain in animals. The dog was chosen because of the accumulated information on its general physiological and behavioural features which have been intensively studied over the last century. The dog is an excellent subject for developmental studies, being easy to handle throughout its life and remaining 'mother-dependent' for a considerable time after birth. In spite of the large amount of neurophysiological work carried out on the dog from Pavlov to Sherrington, from Beck and Práwdicz-Neminski to Baglioni and Amantea amongst others, detailed information about developmental aspects of the central nervous system of the dog is not easily found, the cat having been used more extensively in this connection. Detailed information, for example, about myelination of the dog's brain at various ages is very limited, and a short paper by Döllken in 1898 suggests that there may be only an incomplete parallelism between the myelination of the brain of the cat and that of the dog. Again, data on cranio-cerebral relationships in the dog began to appear only recently, and the measurements in stereotactic atlases are presented only for adult animals. Data on skull and brain growth in terms of volume and direction of expansion are difficult to come by and, in their absence, the accuracy of topographic studies of the electrical activity of the brain in the growing animal, using implanted electrodes, appears very limited. Information about evolution of electroencephalographic (EEG) patterns in the growing dog is not extensive, with somewhat divergent views (Charles and Fuller, Pampiglione and Werner).

This booklet is based on personal observations carried out over a 5-year period as a part-time research worker in the Medical Research Council, Human Nutrition Research Unit at Mill Hill. In addition to the evolution of EEG patterns in the dog from the neonatal period to the end of the first year of post-natal life, some elementary information is included on cranio-cerebral relationships, on brain weights, techniques of recording, and on gross stages of myelination of the cerebral hemispheres. Some modifications of the effect of drugs on the EEG at various ages are briefly mentioned and, in addition, a few examples of abnormal EEG patterns are included. A few common extracerebral bio-electrical phenomena ('artefacts') peculiar to the dog, in contrast with human EEG, are illustrated so that the beginner might acquire sufficient basic information to proceed further through his everyday practical experience. The illustrations are selected from a total of 1,882 EEGs taken from 148 young dogs at variable intervals, from the first few hours of extra-uterine life to the beginning of sexual maturity.

The large majority of the dogs were born and bred in the Unit, mostly from Beagle and Basset stock. Two litters of Boxers were also used, together with a dozen mongrels. Mother-fed and artificially fed animals on good diets were studied as well as animals fed on particular types of deficient diets. The behavioural and feeding habits of the dogs, their rate of growth, the use of disinfestation and of immunization procedures were noted in the history of each animal as part of the usual routine of the Unit. The EEG studies in a sense were incidental to the running of the colony of dogs.

Recently Cammermeyer has drawn attention to the pitfalls of using stray mongrel dogs as experimental animals. His observations were carefully considered in our histological investigations carried out on the brain and spinal cord of particular groups of animals. The satisfactory breeding conditions and the nutritional supervision of the Unit made it possible over the years to obtain adequate clinical information as to the general state of health and growth (including a variety of intercurrent illnesses) of the experimental animals, and care was taken not to include in the group any 'stray mongrel dog'. Whether the term 'usual' should be substituted for 'normal' in contrast to the obviously 'diseased' animal is a question of definitions outside the scope of this small booklet.

A minimum of technical detail is included, as it is presumed that the reader is already familiar with the use of high gain amplifiers and ink-recording apparatus commonly used in EEG work. The method of recording was evolved primarily for long-term EEG studies in nutritional experiments in a variety of laboratory animals, but was also employed in a series of pharmacological experiments and in various other unpublished studies involving scalp recording from the dog during cardio-pulmonary bypass, surface electromyography, and simple electrocardiographic observations in various animals, and occasionally in children at various ages.

When reliable methods for the telemetering of biological data, and particularly of the EEG, become available, a new range of studies will be possible in freely moving animals in a much greater variety of natural conditions; this booklet will then have to be revised. I shall be grateful in the meantime for any comments and suggestions from the readers, to whom my apologies are due for any unintentional omissions.

It is a great pleasure to acknowledge the friendly advice and help of Professor B. S. Platt, as this work would not have been possible without the facilities of his M.R.C. Human Nutrition Research Unit, extended to me for all these years. In the Unit, I am particularly indebted to Mr. Christopher Friend, Mr. R. F. Preece, and Mr. R. J. C. Stewart, for their indefatigable assistance. I would like also to mention that our friend, Professor Alfred Meyer, helped us all in the interpretation of the histological findings of the brains and spinal cords of dogs in this series. The EEG apparatus and part of the running expenses were provided by a generous grant from the National Spastics Society (Medical Research Trust Fund).

I am also indebted for some bibliographical information to Dr. N. P. Bechtereva (Leningrad) and to Dr. Zanocco (Modena), and last, but not least, to the patience of the staff of Butterworths, and to my secretary, Miss Vera Garland.

Cranio-cerebral Relationships in the Growing Animal and Myelination

In the neonatal period, and for a long time thereafter, the scalp of the pup is extremely loose. On palpation, the orbital ridges and the occipital protuberance are just recognizable through the relatively thick and wrinkled scalp. The skull vault is rather thin and the frontal sinuses are very small. The following illustrations (*Figures 1–4*) show the main changes in cranio-cerebral relationships in the growing dog. In addition to the increasing volume of the cavity of the skull which accommodates the growing brain, and to the considerable increase in size of the facial bones, the position of the anterior portion of the

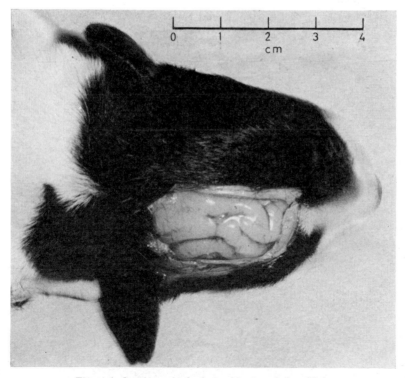

Figure 1. Cranio-cerebral relationships in a 2-day-old dog

1

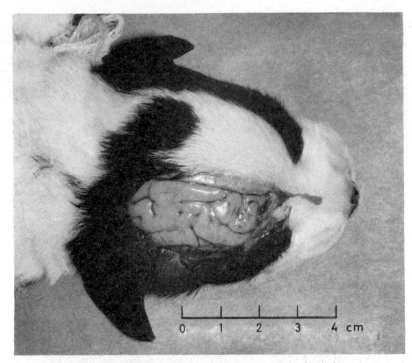

Figure 2. Cranio-cerebral relationships in a 2-week-old dog

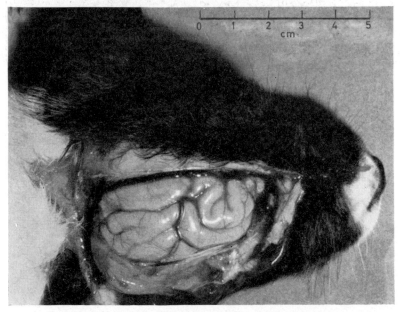

*Figure 3. Cranio-cerebral relationships in a 6-week-old dog.
The cerebral convolutions and sulci are now well formed*

2

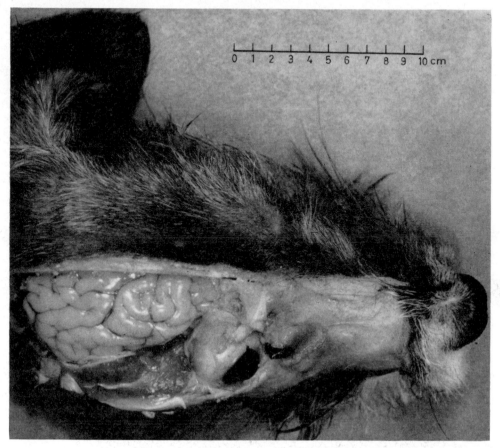

Figure 4. Cranio-cerebral relationships in an adult dog (16 months)

brain in relation to the coronal plane through the centre of the eyeballs appears as if displaced backwards by the growth of the frontal sinuses.

Figure 1 shows the right cerebral hemisphere of a two-day-old pup exposed, while the skull and scalp of the left side are left in place. The brain for the first week or two is soft, somewhat jelly-like to touch, and the convolutions and sulci are poorly formed. The frontal poles are well forward, nearly at the level of the eyelids, while the frontal sinuses are not yet developed.

In *Figure 2*, a similar dissection was made on a dog at the age of 2 weeks. The cerebral convolutions appear only very slightly better formed, while the sulci are slightly more obvious than at the time of birth.

Figure 3 shows a similar dissection on a dog at the age of 6 weeks. There has been a considerable development of the convolutions, and the sulci are well

3

recognizable. The position of the brain, with respect to the coronal plane through the centre of the eyeballs, appears as if displaced backwards. By this time, the occipital protuberance and the orbital ridges are well formed and the scalp is less loose.

In *Figure 4*, a similar dissection in a young adult dog at the age of 16 months shows the final cranio-cerebral relationships comparable to those described in the stereotactic atlases of the adult dog.

Because of the limited information as to the myelination of the cerebral hemispheres in the dog, coronal sections of one hemisphere of four dogs at the ages of 1, 4, 6 and 10 weeks, stained for myelin, are shown (*Figure 5*). Completion of myelination does not appear to occur uniformly in the brain of the dog, but at about 10 weeks of age the staining is well distributed in the white matter of most convolutions.

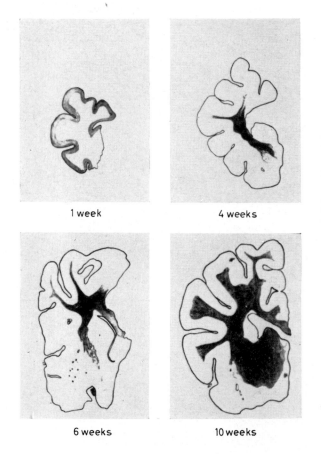

Figure 5. Sketch of myelin staining of a coronal section of a cerebral hemisphere of dog at the ages of 1, 4, 6 and 10 weeks

Electrodes, Their Placement, and Methods of Recording

Because of the changes in cranio-cerebral relationships over the first few weeks and months of life, the location of electrodes implanted in the brain soon after birth would vary considerably in any long-term EEG study. The same difficulty would be met if, instead of electrodes implanted in the brain, an artificial skull vault were fitted to support extradural single or multiple electrodes. In addition, the mothers strongly resent any interference with their newly born pups, and suckling might not be resumed after operations on the head, thus making necessary very early artificial feeding, with all its difficulties. The ranges of weight of the brain (including brain stem and cerebellum) in a small number of animals of comparable litters at various ages are shown in the Table. The

Table of Brain and Body Weights at Various Ages

Dog No.	Sex	Age	Brain weight (g)	Body weight (g)
209	M	1 day	9·5	360
210	M	1 day	8·3	308
440	M	3 days	10	—
442	M	5 days	12·3	465
357	M	1 week	13·5	509
359	M	1 week	14·85	659
443	M	8 days	14·5	554
300	F	3½ weeks	40	1,172
361	F	3½ weeks	36·4	1,650
256	M	4 weeks	37·5	—
258	F	4½ weeks	45	—
391	M	4½ weeks	43	1,850
254	F	4½ weeks	45	—
213	F	8 weeks	55	2,500
242	F	2 months	60	3,600
243	F	2 months	69	3,500
416	M	3 months	73	—
66	M	3 months	72	2,955
143	M	3 months	72	—
145	M	3 months	69	—
159	M	6 months	74	8,000
332	M	6 months	66	—
333	M	6 months	78	—
334	M	6 months	64	—
201	M	1 year	77·2	9,900
202	M	1 year	80·8	11,400

rate of growth of the brain appears to decrease rapidly after the age of about two months, while the increase in body weight continues for a much longer period.

Taking into consideration these and other points, there seems to be no fully satisfactory method of ensuring that in the growing animal the electrical activity of the same regions of the brain is recorded through the skull without the risks of repeated operations. Our knowledge of the origins of the electrical activity of the brain is still extremely limited, and although great accuracy in the placement of electrodes may be necessary in detailed studies of particular regions, this is less important in a broad survey of evolving patterns of activity of large parts of the brain. A regretful acceptance of limited accuracy in electrode placement had to be made in favour of a simple and safe method that would allow repeated EEG observations in the growing animal over periods of months and years. Because of the looseness of the scalp in early life and the type of its movements in young dogs, the use of several separate electrodes was considered preferable to that of multiple electrodes fixed together in a rigid framework. In order to maintain a fairly uniform plan in the distribution of the electrodes, the scalp was considered as if divided into three antero-posterior areas on each side of the midline from the orbital ridge to the level of the occipital protuberance. A total of 6 electrodes on the scalp, plus an earthing electrode, was considered to be the minimum desirable number. The selected sites were on either side of the midline about the centre of the right and left anterior, middle, and posterior third of each hemisphere (*Figure 6*). Additional electrodes were placed on the scalp utilizing these main landmarks.

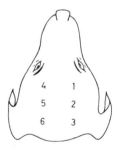

Figure 6. Each number indicates the position of an electrode. This layout has been used throughout this study

Measurements of the distances between electrodes on the scalp were noted on each record, and with a few weeks' practice, the errors both in lateral symmetry and antero-posterior distribution of the electrodes in dogs of similar age and litters were found to be of the order of 1 to 3 mm. In the newly born dog (*see Figure 6*) the distance between the anterior (1–4) and the posterior (3–6) electrodes on either side was 2–2½ cm, while the electrodes in the coronal plane were about 1–1·3 cm from the midline, both anteriorly and posteriorly. In the fully grown dogs, the distance between anterior and posterior electrodes

(1–3 and 4–6) increases to 5 or 6 cm, while the distance between each anterior electrode (1 and 4) and the midline increased only to about $1 \cdot 6 - 2 \cdot 5$ cm; and that between each posterior electrode and the midline increased to about $2 \cdot 5 - 2 \cdot 8$ cm. These figures varied to a certain extent in relation to breed and individual sizes of head examined and would not be valid for other smaller, or larger, breeds.

After various attempts, satisfactory records could be obtained employing as electrodes small, curved half-circle stainless steel needles as used by plastic surgeons. Lane's cleft-palate needles with cutting edge were soldered to a light, flexible tinsel wire (deaf-aid wire) as in *Figure 7*. The finely braided wire is

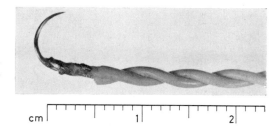

Figure 7. 'Lane's cleft-palate' needle electrode soldered to a double cord 'deaf-aid' wire. Scale in cm. Note the straight soldered joint

PVC covered. Double cord was found reasonably flexible and far more robust than single cord. It was important to solder the wire to the needle without a bend so that any pull on either the needle or its lead would be transmitted to the strongest part of the junction. Half a dozen of these small needle electrodes could be applied by hand in less than half a minute with a minimum of practice. The needles did not appear to be noticed by most animals, provided they were not inserted more than a millimetre or two into the thickness of the skin. A deeper insertion was often resented and appeared to stimulate an undesirable activity of scalp muscles. The electrodes would remain in place even during fairly brisk movements of the animals. In some of the experimental animals on a deficient diet, with an apparently very sensitive skin, for example, during some phases of vitamin B_1 deficiency, the use of a surface analgesic paste as employed by dentists was found very useful (Xylotox Paste). In the early experiments, collodion was used to give greater stability to the electrode–skin contact, but this was found rather cumbersome, and some of the animals appeared to be disturbed by the evaporating and stinging ether, so that all the records of this study were taken without any additional fixing of the electrodes. Stainless steel needles were found to be far superior to carbon steel needles and could be used many times over a period of several weeks, although sharpness tended to fall after about a dozen insertions. Although the needles were not sterilized, no local scalp infection was met, even in animals who had several dozen records taken over a period of weeks and months. A small haematoma of the scalp at the site of insertion of the needle was a rare occurrence in the early phases of evolution of this method of recording, and did not occur for the last 3 years or more, since greater proficiency in superficial insertion of the needles was achieved.

During the tests, the very young animals were held either in a box on cotton wool or in the hand. As the dog grew in size, it was held in a comfortable position on the lap of the laboratory assistant. One hand of the assistant was usually rested on the animal's back and the other either under the chin, to relax the extensor muscles of the head and neck, or around the muzzle just over the eyelids to occlude vision for appropriate periods (*see Figures 8–13*).

Figure 8. Layout of electrodes and method of supporting the head of a very young pup (2 days old)

With this type of stainless steel needle electrodes, the contact resistance with the skin was high, of the order of 50–100 kΩ. With apparatus of relatively low input impedance it was often difficult to obtain satisfactory records from the scalp as other potential changes would appear in the traces, superimposed on those of the cerebral activity. However, when commercial apparatus with sufficiently high input impedance became available, the records were greatly improved. The great majority of EEGs were recorded with an amplification factor of 10 μV/mm pen deflection, that is to say, usually at 100 μV/cm calibration signal. The gain, when necessary, was either reduced or increased to the same extent in all channels (with a master gain control). The electrocardiogram was recorded through similar electrodes gently inserted in the skin of the forelimbs, the amplification being of the order of 40–80 μV/mm

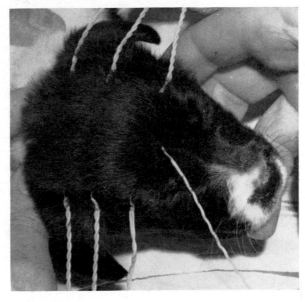

Figure 9. Layout of electrodes and method of supporting the head of a 2-week-old pup

pen deflection. The time constant was 0·3 sec, and the full HF response of the apparatus was employed most of the time (linear within 10 per cent up to 80c/s). The paper speed was usually either 30 or 15 mm/sec. Although some of the EEGs were taken with other ink-recording apparatus, all the tracings

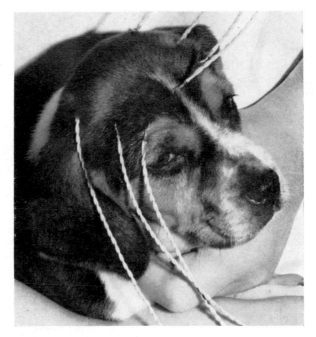

Figure 10. Layout of electrodes and resting position of the head in a 6-week-old pup

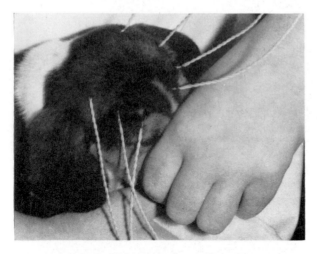

Figure 11. Same dog as in Figure 10. Eyes partly exposed during sleep

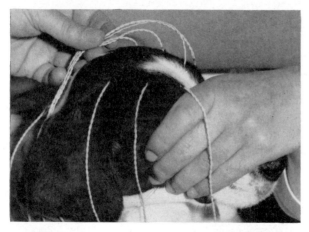

Figure 12. Layout of electrodes in an adult dog (1 year old). Correct position of the hand covering fully the eyelids

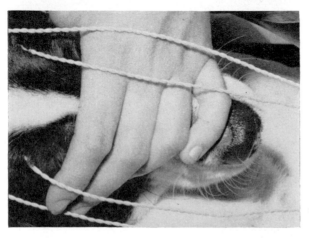

Figure 13. Same dog as in Figure 12. Detail to show an insufficient occlusion of the animal's vision (dog peeping with left eye)

for this study were taken with an O.T.E. (Galileo) 4-channel R32T apparatus. Because of lack of space, the animals had to be tested in the same room in which the recording apparatus was used, and often the young dogs appeared very interested in the testing gear. This was probably one of the reasons why records during spontaneous sleep became the exception after the age of about 4–5 months and the animals would remain awake, though quiet, for hours, probably listening to the slight noise of the paper coming out of the EEG apparatus, although vision was occluded by the hand of the assistant covering the eyelids.

Normal Evolution of EEG Patterns

The following series of illustrations is a selection of samples from long EEG records. It is an attempt to provide a visual presentation of the evolution of features predominant in particular age groups, from the first few hours to the end of the first year of extra-uterine life of the dog. In this series of illustrations, some animals are followed up through EEGs taken at several stages of evolution; however, both to emphasize particular aspects of the evolution of the patterns and to give information about individual variations, the EEGs of other dogs are often interpolated. Whenever possible, examples are given of changes in the patterns during various degrees of alertness or during sleep, either in the same animal or in others of the same age. A chronological order is followed throughout this part of the study, and no attempt is made to explain why particular changes do occur in the patterns of the electrical activity of the brain as the animal grows older.

The evolution of EEG patterns in this series of animals appeared to parallel to a considerable extent the early stages of 'development of social behaviour' of puppies, as described by Scott and Marston in 1950: 'Neonatal Period' (0–2 weeks); 'Transition Period' (2–3½ weeks); 'Period of Socialization' (3½ weeks to 8–10 weeks). However, their 'juvenile period' (8–10 weeks to 7–14 months) does not appear to be a uniform stage when considered from the electroencephalographic aspect, as a noticeable change was seen in most animals at about 4–5 months of age. This would correspond approximately to the beginning of the 'pre-pubertal' stage of Menzel and Menzel (1937).

The technique of recording with the animal in contact most of the time with the hands of one of the observers has some advantages in contrast with other more remote methods of recording. In addition to the simple visual observation of the behaviour of the animal, this method makes it possible to 'feel' its state of neuromuscular activity when the animal becomes tense, or relaxed, appears interested, is just trying to change position, becomes drowsy, or falls definitely asleep, either quietly or twitching, shivering or otherwise moving. In addition, this method makes it possible to occlude the animal's vision for appropriate periods of time without adding too many other stimuli. Simple olfactory, auditory, and tactile stimuli could also be presented without an additional visual stimulus.

In the first month of life, and particularly in the first two weeks, when the eyes of the pup were shut, it was very difficult to discern when the dogs were definitely asleep (or just quiet). Little help could be obtained from the EEG patterns at this stage to learn when a particular change in alertness might have occurred.

12

It was noticed that occasional periods of generalized tremor, or 'shivering' lasting a second or two, would occur in the first few days of life (up to 10–15 days) when the animal was apparently at rest, but not during feeding or when trying to move about. It was assumed that this phenomenon might be parallel to what is commonly observed in very young pigs, which, during the 'shivering periods' are obviously asleep. Apart from this distinction of doubtful validity, it was very difficult to recognize sleep, in contrast to being at rest, from the behaviour of the young pups before the age of 11–14 days, that is to say, before the age at which the dog is able to keep his eyes open. From this age onwards there appear to be clearly recognizable periods (or cycles) during which the animal may remain awake, though quiet, or fall asleep.

In evaluating the effect of various natural stimuli (hand clapping or finger clicking, noise of a spoon in a cup, or in a metal food container, various olfactory and tactile stimuli, changing the illumination of the room, etc.), the behavioural response and the occurrence of detectable changes in the EEG had to be evaluated quite separately. The two phenomena, though parallel after about the first month of extra-uterine life, seemed to be somewhat independent in the first few weeks of age.

In the first few months of life of the dog in general, the evolution of the EEG patterns was not continuous but appeared to occur in steps; that is to say, for fairly long periods of days or weeks only minor variations would be seen and then over a relatively short period of time the patterns would change into those of a successive developmental stage. These developmental (or evolutional) steps are uneven in degree and duration, and tend to appear at about the same age for different litters taken as a group, although individual variations even within a litter are common. The changes in the appearance of the EEG occurring for example at about 8 days, at 3–4 weeks, at 7–8 weeks, or at $4\frac{1}{2}$–5 months, would not appear on the very same day in each member of a litter, but on the whole would occur over a period of a few days only, rather than being scattered over weeks and months. In this connection, it was noted that a member of a litter who was the first one of his group to show an early change in the EEG at the age of 7 days (instead of 8), might not necessarily be the first one of his own litter to show the subsequent changes of EEG patterns, for example, at 7–8 weeks or at $4\frac{1}{2}$–5 months.

No marked differences in the evolution of EEG patterns were noted between male and female pups when considered over a long period of time, although slightly greater variations might occur at critical periods such as the 7–8 weeks one. The trend was for the young bitches to be slightly more forward than the males, although individual variations even within a litter were great. The animals were tested usually after being fed, as in general it was noted that, after the age of weaning, the pups were much quieter with a full than with a relatively empty belly. This difference in behaviour was even more obvious for those animals in whom artificial feeding had begun at the age of about 3 weeks, and in these pups, sleep rarely occurred during the couple of hours

13

preceding a feed. Slight differences in behaviour, and to a certain extent in the EEG features, could be noticed within the same litter between pups who had been mother-fed and those who had artificial feeding. The trend was towards earlier and more marked differences between waking and sleeping patterns in the mother-fed animals. This might well be due to the fact that the mother-fed animals had a full belly most of the time, while the 're-filling' of the artificially fed animals had to follow a time-table slightly more convenient to the attendant than to the individual metabolic requirements of each pup. The appearance of rhythmic 4–6 c/s activity towards the end of the second month tended to occur nearly a week earlier in many of the mother-fed than in the artificially fed members of the same litter. This seemed to be a trend rather than a constant rule, and again individual variations were common. Much more extensive work would be required to check on several of the above-mentioned incomplete observations.

Moderate asymmetries between the activities of the two hemispheres in apparently normally born and bred dogs were often seen, both in the form of differences in overall amplitude or in the amount of faster activities mixed with the slow elements. Gross asymmetries, however, were not seen in the present series of normal animals.

In relation to the general behaviour of the animal, there were no appreciable, or constant, differences in amplitude and frequency of the dominant rhythms between dogs that appeared active and restless, and dogs that were either quiet or whining. There were, however, considerable differences between animals in relation not only to their individual response to a simple stimulus, but particularly to their ability to adapt to the repetition of the same stimulus. This individual peculiarity, both as behavioural and EEG phenomena, often persisted in the same animal through various phases of its development. It would be of considerable theoretical, and probably practical, interest to plan prospective developmental and behavioural studies to assess what are the earliest stages at which EEG patterns of either 'rapid' or 'delayed' adaptation to various stimuli might be formed in the dog and other animals.

Throughout the present series of observations, an attempt was made to study the effect of various simple stimuli upon the EEG at various ages. It was soon noticed that, in spite of considerable individual differences, both visual and auditory stimuli evoked only minor and inconsistent EEG changes during the first 3–3½ weeks of life, both during sleep and during the waking state. Occasionally, a startle reaction might be seen without, however, any detectable EEG change. Later, however, and particularly after the end of the first month, similar stimuli were usually followed by marked changes in the EEG. The type and extent of this phenomenon depended partly on the state of the animal at the time, and partly on some quality of the stimulus, its novelty or its repetition. When the animal at 2–4 months of age was awake and resting, with eyes covered (or closed), rhythmic 4–6 c/s activity would be blocked by a noise, by a tactile, or by an olfactory stimulus, with an increase in low amplitude faster activities. When the animal was asleep, clear K-complexes, comparable with those described in man and other animals, usually followed an auditory stimulus after the age of about 4–5 weeks.

Olfactory stimuli (smell of food) and mixed ones (smell of acetone or ether) were, however, quite effective even during the first few weeks of life. The behavioural changes in response to an olfactory stimulus were more obvious than the EEG changes, particularly in the first 2–3 weeks of life. Often, both the motor and the EEG response would appear with a delay of a few seconds.

Tactile stimuli were occasionally effective even in the first month of life, but seemed to produce a greater EEG change after the second month of life. The effect of visual stimuli could not be systematically tested with our method of holding the animal, as usually the eyes were kept covered by the assistant's hand, the removal of which was in itself a powerful stimulus. However, when vision was occluded temporarily, clear EEG changes (appearance of rhythmic 4–6 c/s activity over the posterior half of the head) could be noted, beginning at 5–6 weeks, and becoming very marked between 8 and about 16–20 weeks. After the end of 5 months, however, the temporary occlusion of vision, even if the animal remained very quiet, was followed by a more limited appearance of, or increase in, rhythmic activity. As judged by their global effect on the EEG, therefore, the responses to particular modalities of stimulation appeared to vary according to the age of the dog; moreover, not all types of stimuli appeared to be followed by EEG changes of similar entity at all ages. This might suggest that there is some kind of scale of values for categories of stimuli which is valid, however, only over a particular period of development of cerebral function. Perhaps more detailed anatomical and histochemical studies might give a clue to this peculiar variability in the effect of stimuli at various ages, during the early phases of maturation of cerebral function.

First Week of Extra-Uterine Life *(Figures 14-28)*

The EEGs taken 9–12 hours after birth do not appear to be substantially different from those taken 2–7 days later in the same animals. The most important feature is the discontinuity of rhythmic activity and the independent appearance of activity in one or the other region of each hemisphere, either over the anterior or over the posterior half of the head. Between runs of activity, the traces become nearly flat (equipotential) for a couple of seconds or longer. On occasions, these periods of relative silence would last in a particular region slightly longer than elsewhere, giving an impression, for a period, of considerable asymmetry between the activities of homologous regions of the two hemispheres. This degree of asymmetry might persist for many seconds, on occasions up to 20 or 30 sec, but then the asymmetry might be reversed and another region might become less active for a period of time. Taken over a period of several minutes, no persistent differences could be detected between activities recorded from the anterior or from the posterior electrodes on the scalp or from the right or the left hemisphere. Thus no obvious changes could be recognized in the EEG when the animal appeared relaxed and quiet (as if asleep), when the animal was moving about or whimpering (as if awake), or when the animal showed prolonged bouts of twitching, or shivering (probably during sleep).

The overall amplitude of the traces was about 30–50 μV, and most of the rhythmic activity which appeared in runs was at about 5–7 and 12–15 c/s. Marked changes in illumination of the closed eyelids, sudden noises, or tactile stimuli applied at various intervals, did not appear to be followed by detectable EEG changes. On occasions, olfactory stimuli, and particularly mixed ones (smell of ether or acetone), might be followed by a slightly prolonged period of flattening of the traces over both hemispheres, but this response did not appear to be a constant one.

During this phase, the pups are unable to walk or to open their eyes, but may crawl towards the breast and suck vigorously for fairly long periods. With apparent considerable effort they may turn upright if placed on their back, can lift their head and tend to keep it horizontally for short periods. On occasions, they might turn the head towards (or away from) the source of an olfactory or tactile stimulus, but there is no recognizable response to a loud noise or to a flash of light. As previously mentioned, it was found very difficult at this age to assess when the animal should be considered to be definitely asleep.

Second and Third Weeks (Figures 29–34)

At the age of 6–8 days, the EEG patterns change from the discontinuous to a continuous type of activity. In most animals the short periods of relative equipotentiality seen during the first week of life disappear completely in a day or two. In general, the activity becomes of a somewhat lower amplitude (20–40 μV), with considerable individual variations, with a predominance of rhythmic 10–15 c/s waves and less regular slower waves. At the age of about 11–14 days, when most dogs begin to open their eyes, there seems to be no gross modification in EEG patterns whether the animals have their eyelids closed or open. Moreover, while the behavioural differences between alertness and sleep become less difficult to recognize, the occasional changes in the EEG features in these states are only slight and do not seem to be clearly parallel to the behaviour of the animal. No sleep spindles were seen during this period and only inconsistent EEG changes were elicited in response to auditory, visual and tactile stimuli. Changes in amplitude and occasionally in frequency of the activity over both hemispheres were, however, seen occasionally in response to olfactory stimuli.

On the whole, towards the end of the third week, there was an increase in slow components in the EEG and in particular there were distinct periods during which either the fast or the slow components would predominate.

These changes, however, were not strictly parallel to behavioural changes and did not seem to be related to responses to recognizable environmental factors. Either the fast or the slow components might predominate for long periods during which the animal seems to be in a similar state of sleep.

During the whole of this period, the motor control of the animal evolves rapidly and, in addition to the opening of the eyelids and to the improved orientation of head movements, the animal begins to walk, can hold his head in a fairly steady position, and can turn over quickly when placed on his back.

End of the First Month (*Figures 35–39*)

At about $3\frac{1}{2}$–4 weeks of age, slow activity at about 2–5 c/s begins to appear though somewhat irregular, and the faster components diminish. The amplitude of the traces increases to 40–80 μV. About this time, more constant EEG changes are seen in relation to sleep, generally with an increase in slow activity. No definite sleep spindles can be identified. Sudden noises during sleep evoke clearly recognizable K-complexes, and similar changes may be elicited also by tactile and visual stimuli during sleep. Olfactory stimuli during sleep usually are followed by behavioural arousal, often preceded by a temporary increase in the amplitude of the slow activity in the EEG. During the waking state, particularly if the animal has the eyes open and looks around, the traces diminish somewhat in amplitude without, however, the predominance of fast components seen either in earlier or later periods of life.

As yet there is no marked difference between the activities recorded over the anterior and over the posterior regions of the two hemispheres. In some animals, there are transitory periods of a few days during which an asymmetry in amplitude between the activities of the two hemispheres becomes apparent. In general, only occasionally rhythmic activity is seen at this age either during sleep or during the waking state.

The pups, in this period, continue to become increasingly interested in their surroundings, become rather less clumsy, begin to growl and are able to orientate their head, nose, eyes, and ears in the appropriate directions. They begin to show more clearly pleasure and fear, alertness and drowsiness, as well as definite sleep. An obvious startle reaction may be elicited by a sudden loud noise.

Fifth and Sixth Weeks (*Figures 40 and 41*)

From the EEG aspect, during this period, some differentiation between the activities of the anterior and the posterior thirds of each hemisphere begins to appear. Although rhythmic activity is not yet well formed during the waking state, an irregular 3–6 c/s activity increases in amplitude over the posterior half of each hemisphere at this age, and the overall amplitude of the traces increases to 60–100 μV. During sleep some rhythmic runs of 6–10 c/s waves begin to appear, usually better formed over the anterior than over the posterior half of the head. Various stimuli during sleep evoke large K-complexes which are usually symmetrical and more obvious over the anterior and middle third of each hemisphere than over its posterior third.

During the waking state, when vision is excluded by placing a hand over the dog's eyelids, there is a slight increase in amplitude of the activity over the posterior half of the head without, however, the appearance of prolonged rhythmic activity. A definite diminution in the amplitude of the traces is seen, however, when the animal, after a period of occluded vision, is allowed to look around. At this age it was noted that the transition between EEG patterns during alertness and those during sleep was in general more rapid in mother-fed animals than in those which were artificially fed.

During this period the dog is nearing the weaning time, becomes stronger, more agile, and sure of its movements, is able to climb out of an open box, and to recognize simple objects, appears fully accustomed to the test situation and is very docile, in spite of the increasing interest in surroundings and in playing about. Pleasure and displeasure can be expressed with recognizable sounds. At about this age, a whistle begins to become an effective stimulus for the animal, both during sleep and during the waking state.

Seventh to Ninth Weeks (Figures 43-45)

Over a period of less than one week, towards the end of the second month, a remarkable change occurs in the EEG, with the appearance of a rhythmic activity at about 4–6 c/s of large amplitude (100–150 or more µV). This activity is seen mostly over the posterior half of each hemisphere and appears only when the animal is awake, quiet, and when vision is occluded by covering the eyes of the animal or closing his eyelids. This rhythmic activity is clearly blocked by visual stimuli. If the animal's eyes are kept covered, this rhythmic activity tends to persist for long periods though waxing and waning. When visual stimuli are excluded, the rhythmic activity may be blocked by other stimuli (tactile, auditory, and olfactory), and on occasions probably also by stimuli of proprioception, gustatory and other kinds. A repetition of the same stimulus is usually followed by a diminution of the 'blocking effect'. If the same stimulus is presented at fairly regular intervals of 10–20 sec, complex effects appear to follow, probably related to phenomena of adaptation and conditioning to the time intervals between stimuli.

This rhythmic activity, though appearing fairly symmetrically over the two hemispheres, shows a variable preponderance on one or the other side when the animal is left apparently undisturbed. Comparing the activity recorded between electrodes placed over the posterior third of each hemisphere with that of other electrode combinations on each hemisphere, it seems probable that some common regulatory processes might be present between the activities of various regions of the cerebral hemispheres. Minor alterations in frequency of the activity over one hemisphere appear to be accompanied by alterations in frequency elsewhere. Moreover, the blocking effect following a brief stimulus appears to occur over both hemispheres at about the same time.

During sleep the rhythmic 4–6 c/s activity over the posterior half of the hemispheres disappears, while generalized, larger slower waves are seen with considerable fluctuations in amplitude. Faster components, often in runs, appear over the anterior half of the head during early sleep. Large K-complexes are easily elicited with a variety of stimuli. Long periods of low amplitude fast activity are seen during sleep unaccompanied by increased eye movements.

At about this age, that is to say before the end of the second month of life, weaning occurs. New objects are systematically investigated with nose, eyes, and mouth, and the animals appear to follow moving objects with their head and eyes fairly quickly. The dogs appear quick to learn simple tasks, and towards the end of the second month appear to recognize the differences between the sleeping place and the feeding place; and often may defecate elsewhere. Both previously tested and previously untested pups appear to be happy to be approached by other dogs and by human beings. While running, usually their front paws and back paws are used together. Tail wagging as a greeting sign begins to be present. The growth of the brain (see Table, brain weights) slows down considerably at the end of the second month of extra-uterine life, and the processes of myelination (as judged by myelin staining techniques) appear to reach completion.

Tenth to Twentieth Weeks (Figures 46–52)

There seems to be little change in the EEG patterns during the third and fourth month of life. The rhythmic activity is well formed at about 4–6 c/s, regular and fairly symmetrical, appearing mostly over the posterior half of the head. Its amplitude is of the order of 100 µV when the animal is awake and when environmental (particularly visual and auditory) stimuli are kept to a minimum. In response to visual and other stimuli, this rhythmic activity may be promptly blocked while lower amplitude faster activities (10–30 c/s) appear. When the animal is alert, looking around and, or, otherwise active and attentive, the traces may remain of low amplitude for many minutes (10–30 µV), with a predominance of relatively faster activities and no trace of the larger amplitude 4–6 c/s rhythmic activity. The difference between the activities of the anterior and the posterior portions of each cerebral hemisphere is better seen during the waking state with excluded vision and during early sleep rather than full alertness. Sleep spindles which began to appear during the second month of life are now more obvious, but do not reach the regularity of those seen in man. K-complexes are easily elicited by a variety of stimuli. Towards the end of the fourth month the amplitude of the traces diminishes. It was difficult with our method of recording to have dogs more than four months old falling asleep spontaneously.

The animals are fully weaned at the beginning of the third month, and, although still somewhat slow and awkward in some movements, their eating and drinking habits are similar to those of adult dogs. During this period, the pups become rapidly more agile and playful, particularly with other members of the litter, but sexual behaviour is still at a rudimentary level. Although bodily growth continues to be fairly rapid over the third month, and also during the fourth month, the cerebral growth slows down considerably during this period, as the size of an adult brain is approached.

Five Months to One Year (Figures 53–57)

This is the last period covered by the present study. During this time, the EEG patterns appear to be fairly uniform. The most important feature is the rapid diminution in the amplitude of the traces at the age of about five months, with some slight change in frequency of the dominant rhythmic activity during the waking state. The traces are usually of an amplitude of about 20–40 μV or less. When the animal is awake, quiet and with vision occluded, the dominant rhythmic activity over the posterior half of the hemisphere is at about 6–8 c/s, of an amplitude of 30–40 μV, often interrupted by runs of activity at 12–14 c/s, usually of lower amplitude. Faster activities, usually of very low amplitude, are also seen, particularly over the anterior half of the head. The 6–8 c/s activity is blocked by visual stimuli and particularly by auditory stimuli when vision is occluded. Tactile and olfactory stimuli are followed by similar responses, although often not so marked.

It was not possible to produce even a reasonable guess as to the probable 'significance' (difference in effects) of various types and modalities of stimulation for each animal. The inferences as to possible comparison of the effect of various stimuli upon the EEG must be considered therefore as extremely vague. Very few normal dogs in this age group fell asleep spontaneously and their general EEG features resembled those described in younger animals, apart from a slight diminution in overall amplitude.

During this long period of life, the dog becomes sexually mature and reaches adult skills, although bodily growth continues for a slightly longer period. The growth of the brain has already reached adult size early in this period.

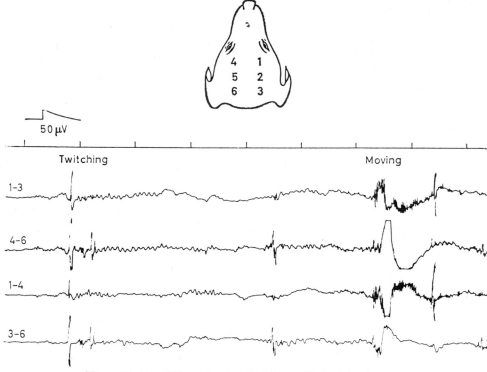

Figure 14. Dog 380—approximately 9 hours old. Periods of activity and periods of relative equipotentiality occur independently in various areas

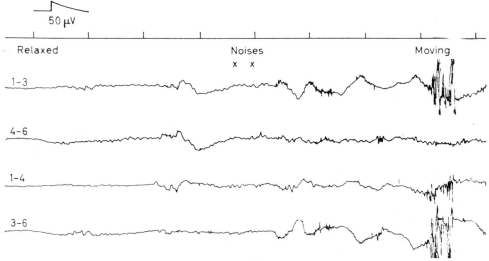

Figure 15. Dog 380—approximately 10 hours old. There is no recognizable change in the EEG in response to loud noises

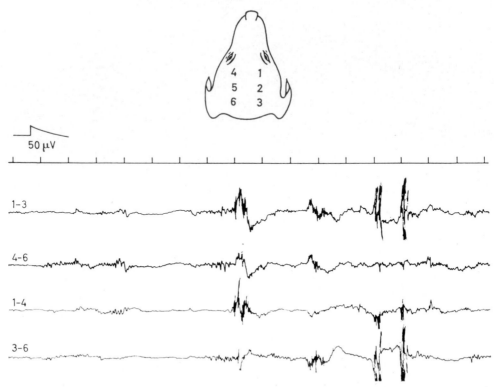

Figure 16. Dog 380—approximately 10 hours old. Record taken at reduced paper speed (15 mm/sec) to show relative independence of bursts of activity in various regions while the animal appears to be awake and moves about

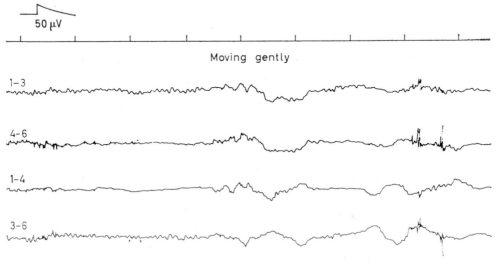

Figure 17. Dog 378—approximately 10 hours old, moving about

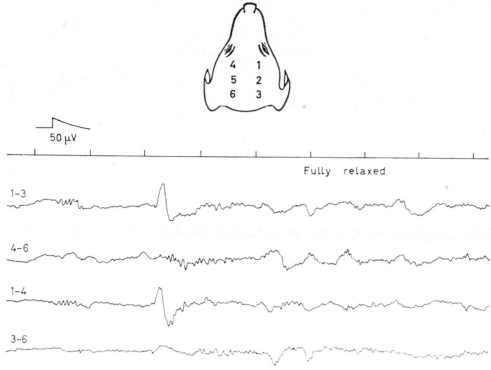

Figure 18. Dog 378—approximately 10 hours old, appears to be still and fully relaxed, perhaps asleep

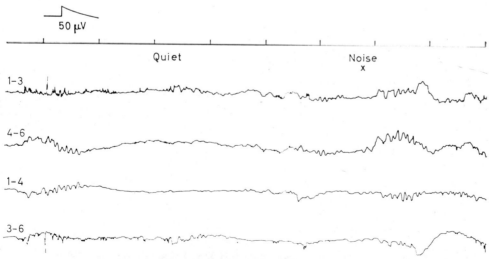

Figure 19. Dog 379—approximately 12 hours old, quiet with occasional twitches, probably asleep. No recognizable EEG change in response to a noise

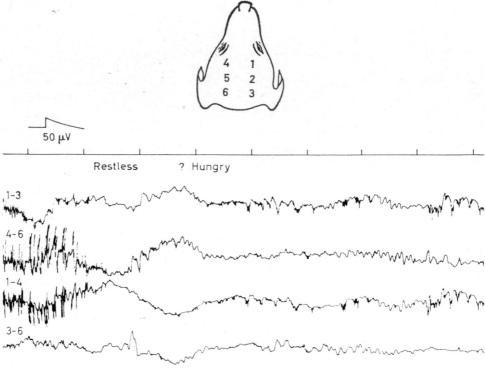

Figure 20. Dog 379—approximately 12 hours old. Restless, moving about, probably hungry

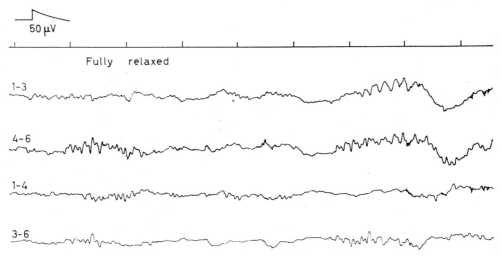

Figure 21. Dog 379—approximately 12 hours old. A few minutes after the previous illustrations (Figures 19 and 20). The pup is now quiet, fully relaxed, perhaps asleep

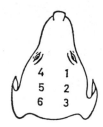

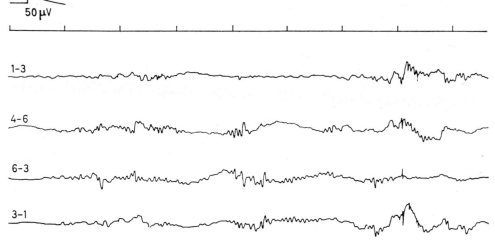

Figure 22. Dog 358—4 days old. The discontinuous activity seen during the first day persists. Here, the animal is quiet, fully relaxed, twitching occasionally, perhaps asleep

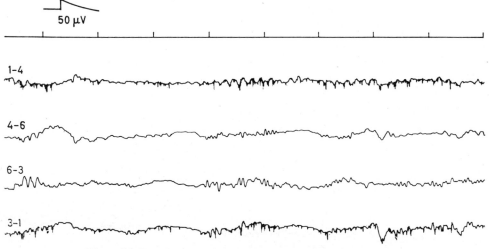

Figure 23. Dog 358—4 days old. The same animal as in Figure 22. Is now moving gently, probably awake. Apart from the muscle action potentials there has been little change in the appearance of the traces

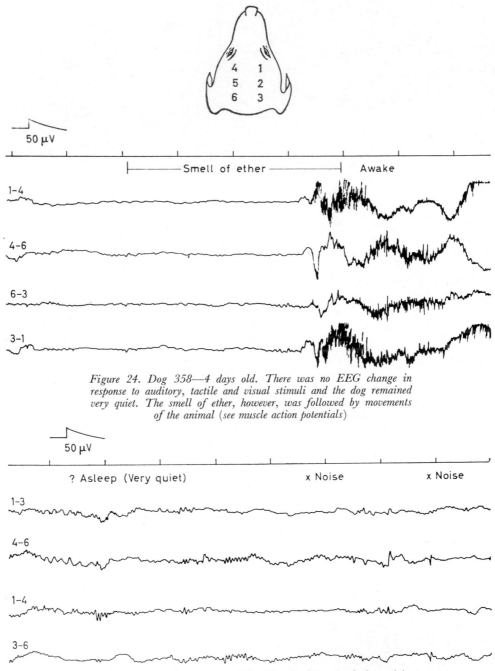

Figure 24. Dog 358—4 days old. There was no EEG change in response to auditory, tactile and visual stimuli and the dog remained very quiet. The smell of ether, however, was followed by movements of the animal (see muscle action potentials)

Figure 25. Dog 383—4 days old. Also in this animal the activity appears discontinuous and with variable distribution. No change in response to noises while resting (? asleep)

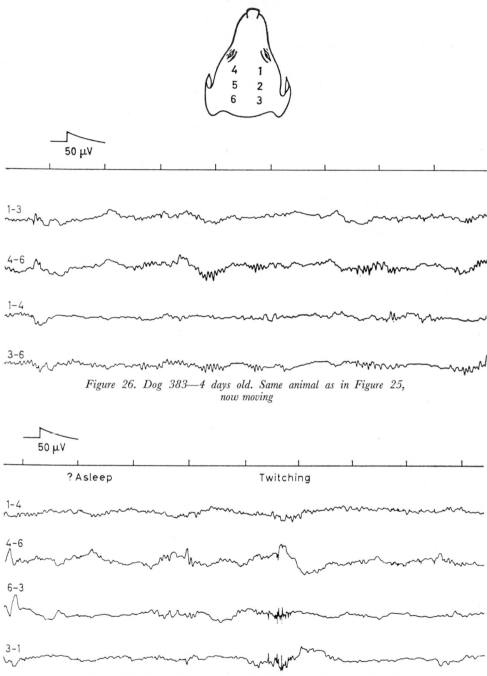

Figure 26. Dog 383—4 days old. Same animal as in Figure 25,
now moving

Figure 27. Dog 358—1 week old. Quiet, twitching occasionally,
probably asleep. The discontinuity of the EEG activity in various
regions persists (see Figures 23 and 24)

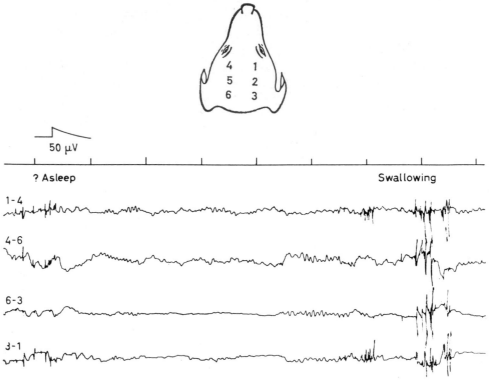

Figure 28. Dog 358—1 week old. A few minutes after Figure 27.
The activity appears still discontinuous

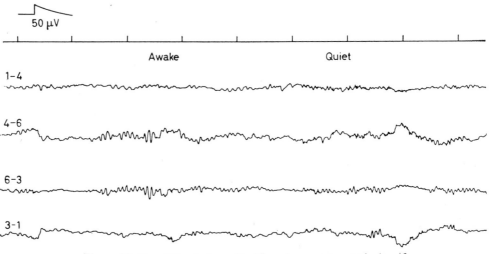

Figure 29. Dog 358—8 days old. There is a greater continuity of
activity in comparison with Figures 27 and 28

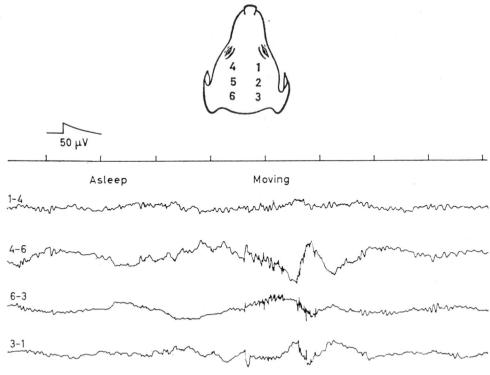

Figure 30. Dog 358—8 days old. A few minutes after Figure 29.
The pup is moving gently as if asleep. The activity is not yet fully
continuous, particularly in some regions

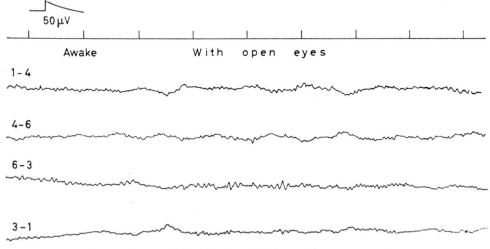

Figure 31. Dog 358—14 days old. The activity is now continuous
in most regions. The animal looks around

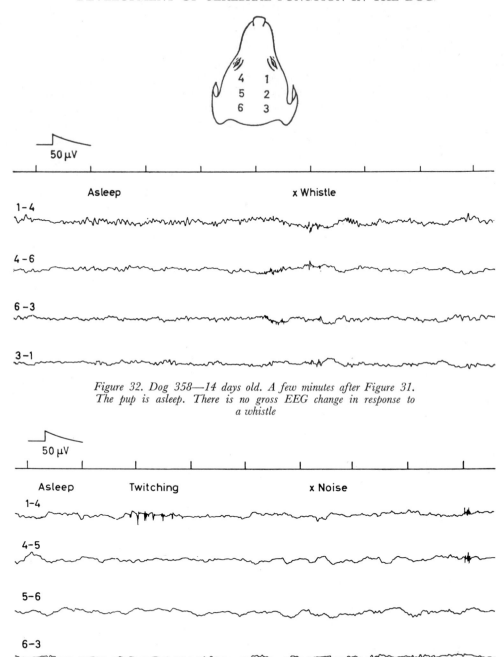

Figure 32. Dog 358—14 days old. A few minutes after Figure 31. The pup is asleep. There is no gross EEG change in response to a whistle

Figure 33. Dog 300—10 days old. The low amplitude fast and slow components are continuous, without periods of equipotentiality. There is no recognizable EEG change in response to a noise (animal relaxed, twitching, probably asleep)

30

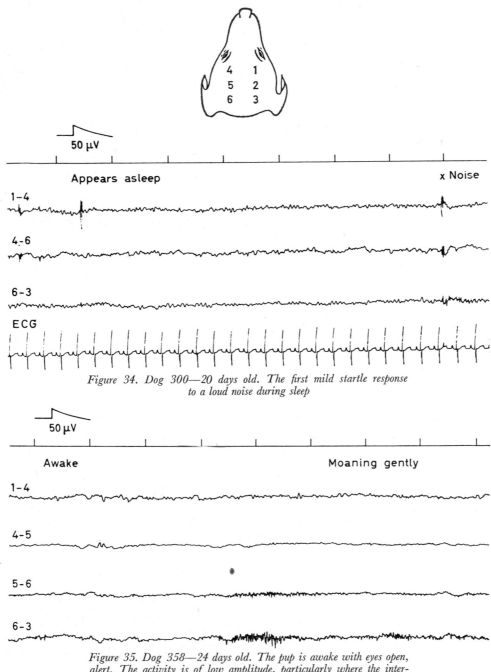

*Figure 34. Dog 300—20 days old. The first mild startle response
to a loud noise during sleep*

*Figure 35. Dog 358—24 days old. The pup is awake with eyes open,
alert. The activity is of low amplitude, particularly where the inter-
electrode distance is small over the same hemisphere; electrodes 4–5
and 5–6 are about 1·3 cm apart, while 1–4 and 6–3 are about
2·5 cm apart*

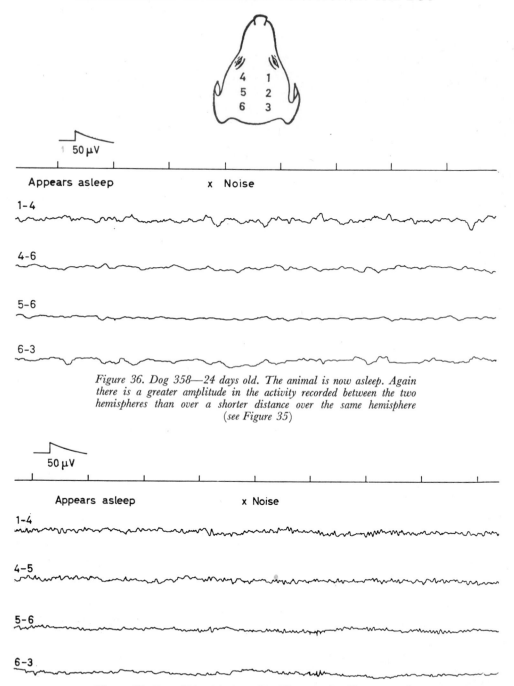

Figure 36. Dog 358—24 days old. The animal is now asleep. Again there is a greater amplitude in the activity recorded between the two hemispheres than over a shorter distance over the same hemisphere (see Figure 35)

Figure 37. Dog 358—24 days old. The animal still seems to be asleep but the EEG features are different from those of Figure 36, there being now a much greater amount of fast components

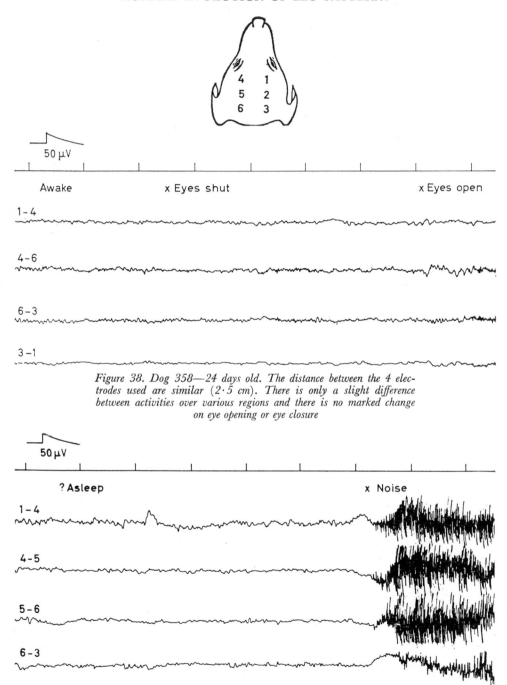

Figure 38. Dog 358—24 days old. The distance between the 4 electrodes used are similar (2·5 cm). There is only a slight difference between activities over various regions and there is no marked change on eye opening or eye closure

Figure 39. Dog 358—1 month old. The dog appears to be asleep but is rapidly alerted by a noise

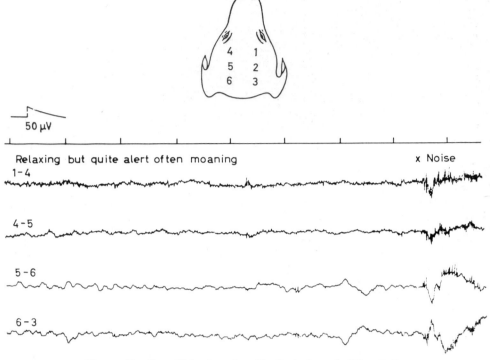

Figure 40. Dog 304—5 weeks old. Beginning of differentiation between activities over the anterior and over the posterior half of the head

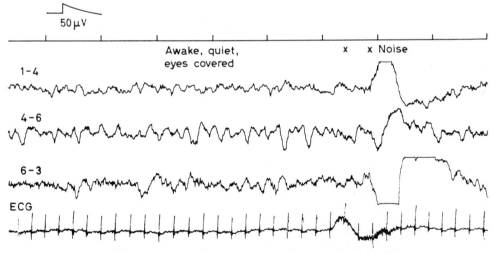

Figure 41. Dog 292—6 weeks old. Overall increase in amplitude of activity in comparison with previous periods. Some irregular 3–5 c/s activity can be recognized with slightly different features between anterior and posterior half of the head

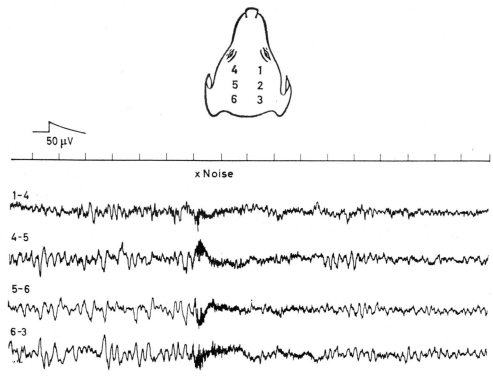

Figure 42. Dog 358—7½ weeks old. Record taken at reduced paper speed. Overall increase in amplitude in comparison with previous periods (see Figures 27–32 and 35–39). The animal is awake but slightly drowsy and moves in response to a noise; while in the EEG slow components are blocked. Rhythmic 4–5 c/s activity returns a few seconds later, better formed over the posterior than over the anterior half of the head. The eyes of the animal were kept covered throughout

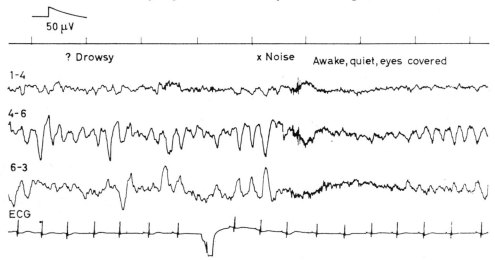

Figure 43. Dog 321—8 weeks old. Awake but drowsy. Similar series of events to Figure 42

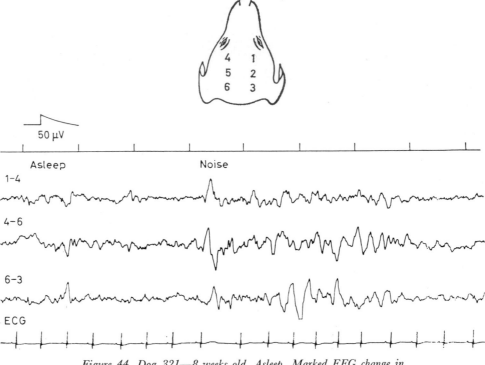

Figure 44. Dog 321—8 weeks old. Asleep. Marked EEG change in
response to a noise (K complex)

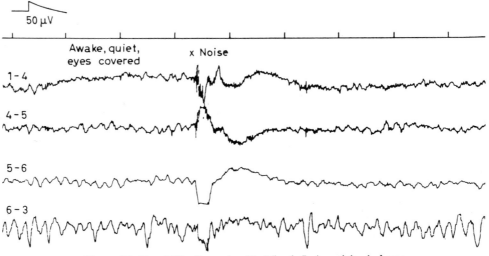

Figure 45. Dog 292—2 months old. The 4–5 c/s activity is larger
over the posterior than over the anterior half of the head. In response
to a noise, there is a startle reaction and a short lived blocking of the
rhythmic activity

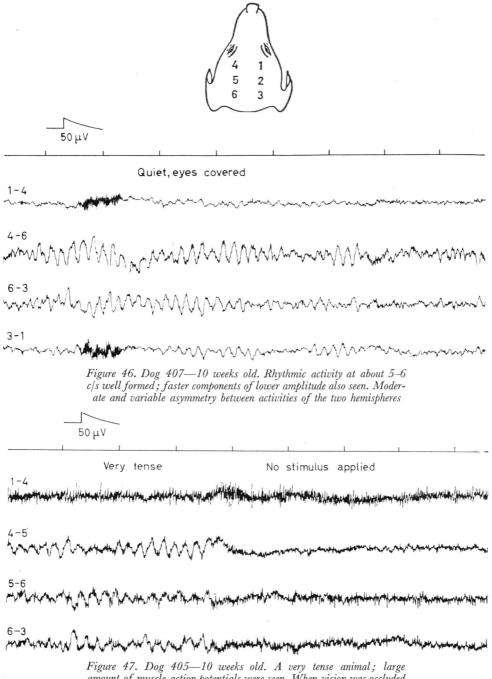

Figure 46. Dog 407—10 weeks old. Rhythmic activity at about 5–6 c/s well formed; faster components of lower amplitude also seen. Moderate and variable asymmetry between activities of the two hemispheres

Figure 47. Dog 405—10 weeks old. A very tense animal; large amount of muscle action potentials were seen. When vision was occluded rhythmic 5 c/s activity appeared for several seconds. It was often blocked 'spontaneously', no obvious stimulus being presented

4

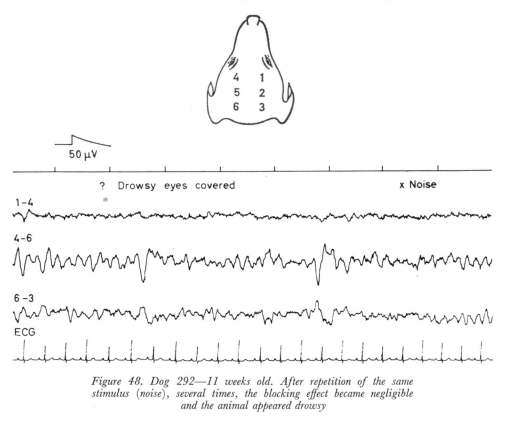

Figure 48. Dog 292—11 weeks old. After repetition of the same stimulus (noise), several times, the blocking effect became negligible and the animal appeared drowsy

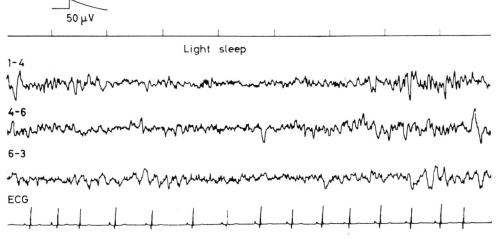

Figure 49. Dog 321—3 months old. During light sleep some 10–15 c/s activity is seen mixed with slower waves. The 'sleep spindles' at about 12–14 c/s are better seen over the anterior than over the posterior half of the head

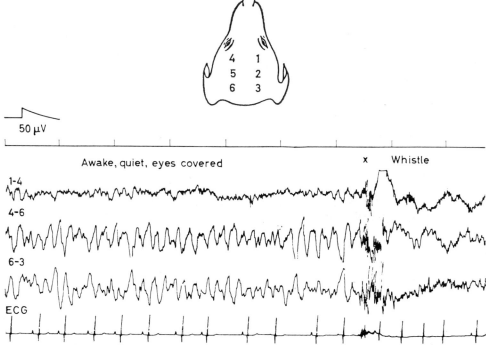

Figure 50. Dog 321—3 months old. When the dog is awake with occluded vision, rhythmic 5 c/s activity predominates over the posterior half of the head mixed with faster elements. In response to a whistle there is a marked startle reaction and the large rhythmic activity is blocked for a while

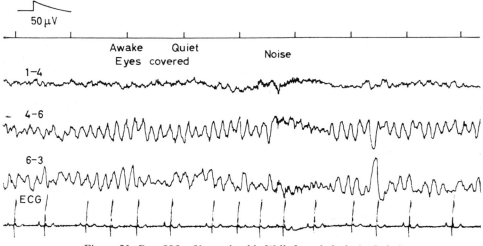

Figure 51. Dog 292—3½ months old. Well formed rhythmic 5–6 c/s activity blocked by a mild auditory stimulus

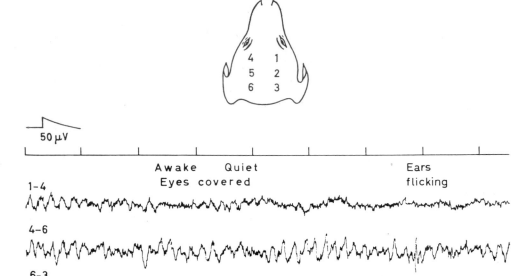

Figure 52. Dog 225—3½ months old. There is a slightly variable distribution of the rhythmic 5-6 c/s activity over the posterior half of the head. This activity is mixed with faster components of lower amplitude. The animal is somewhat tense and muscle action potentials are superimposed upon the EEG

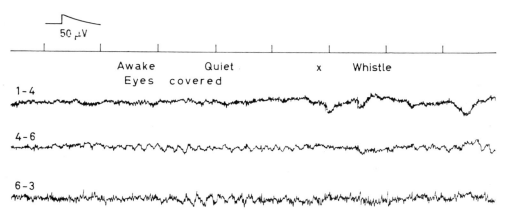

Figure 53. Dog 225—5 months old. The rhythmic activity is now of much lower amplitude and slightly faster at about 6 c/s. It appears when vision is occluded and it is blocked by a noise. The animal is still rather tense

40

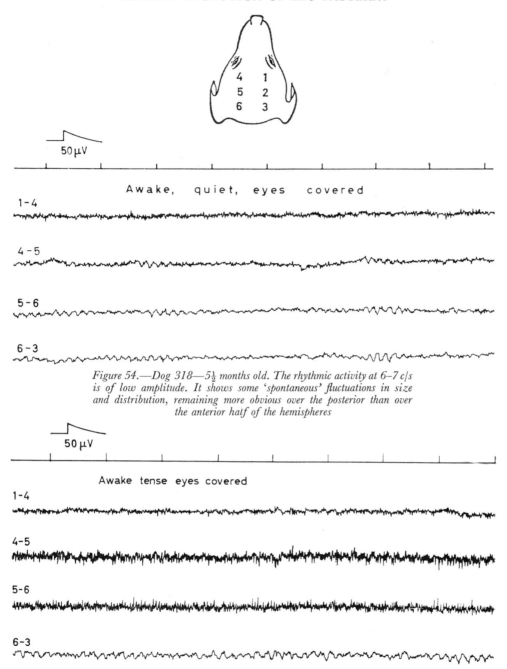

Figure 54.—Dog 318—5½ months old. The rhythmic activity at 6–7 c/s is of low amplitude. It shows some 'spontaneous' fluctuations in size and distribution, remaining more obvious over the posterior than over the anterior half of the hemispheres

Figure 55. Dog 225—6½ months old. The rhythmic activity at 6–7 c/s is of low amplitude mixed with still lower amplitude faster activities. A considerable amount of muscle action potentials is seen in this rather tense animal (see Figures 52 and 53)

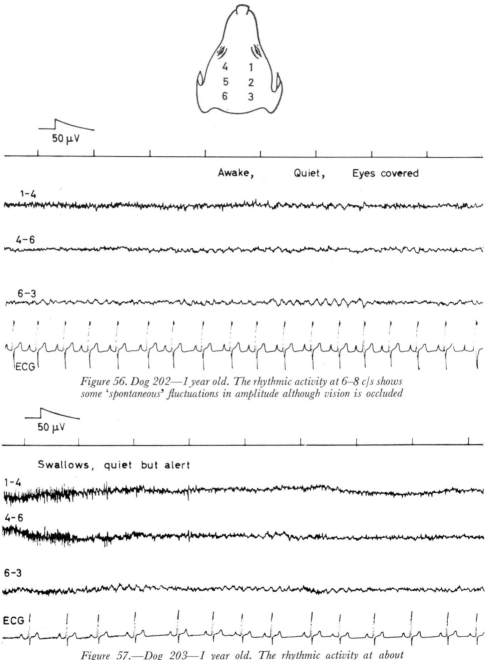

Figure 56. Dog 202—1 year old. The rhythmic activity at 6–8 c/s shows some 'spontaneous' fluctuations in amplitude although vision is occluded

Figure 57.—Dog 203—1 year old. The rhythmic activity at about 6–8 c/s is more prominent over the posterior than over the anterior half of the head and shows spontaneous fluctuations in amplitude. This animal was rather tense and quick to respond to a variety of mild stimuli

Effect of Drugs upon the EEG at Various Ages

The electrical activity of the brain is altered by a variety of drugs affecting the central nervous system. A considerable amount of pharmacological work has been published in the last few years and the EEG of the dog has been extensively used as a means of detecting some of the effects of a variety of drugs. In general, however, such effects are described in dogs of adult or nearly adult age, and little is known of the effect of drugs on the brain of young or very young pups. In this publication, a few illustrations have been included as an introduction to the concept of utilizing the variable effects of drugs on the EEG as another measure of changes in the growing brain. Although much more detailed work will be required with various amounts and kinds of drugs, it has been found that the same drug in a comparable dose (either per body weight or per $\frac{3}{4}$-power body weight) does alter the EEG of dogs in the neonatal period in a way which is quite different from the changes induced either at the age of 4–5 weeks or at the age of about 2 months and thereafter. It is not easy to assess whether these changes in the effect of drugs upon the EEG are related only to phases in the development of cerebral structure and function, or to variations in general metabolic trends, or to changes in circulatory, respiratory and endocrine responses in the first few weeks or months of extra-uterine life. It seems worth emphasizing, however, that another parameter may be added to the study of the development of cerebral function by establishing some approximate landmarks in the evolution of the EEG responses to the same drug at various ages.

For practical reasons of dosage and of easy administration, as well as of margin of safety, a short-acting barbiturate was employed in this study. Sodium thiopentone $2 \cdot 5$ per cent solution was injected in the outer saphenous vein (hind leg) in two doses at an interval of a few minutes. The first intravenous administration was given on the basis of $2 \cdot 5$ mg per kg body weight, while the second dose was either five or ten times larger. The desirable rate of administration was considered to be of about 1 c.c. (25 mg) over 5 sec, although this rate could not always be achieved. Usually, in addition to the EEG (3 channels), an ECG (lead 1) was recorded at the same time. The main evolutional features in the EEG responses to the small and the large dose of the intravenous barbiturate are as follows:

(a) *Stage 1:* before the age of 3–4 weeks, the EEG response to the small dose of intravenous thiopentone consisted of a diminution in the amplitude of the traces beginning 15 sec or so after the injection. There was only a mild increase in the heart rate without gross respiratory changes. After the larger dose, the traces became completely flat within 20 sec. The heart rate increased slightly and there was a period of apnoea lasting nearly half a minute. No fast activity, no sleep spindles, no slow waves, nor periodic 'bursts and silences' appeared in the EEG. Recovery took place in 4–10 minutes, but one animal, of the six tested at this age, did not recover after the large dose and, at necropsy, it was found to have a very small heart.

(b) *Stage 2:* between 3 and 7 weeks, the response to the small dose of intravenous thiopentone was clearly identifiable in the EEG with an increase in rhythmic 7–9 c/s activity, while for the larger dose, after the appearance of a similar activity, slower waves of comparable amplitude and sharp elements were seen. The effect on heart rate and respiration was comparable with that described above. Again, one animal out of seven did not recover after the large dose (a litter mate of the one who died in the previous group).

(c) *Stage 3:* after the age of approximately 2 months, the EEG response is similar to that seen in adult dogs. In response to the small dose of thiopentone, low amplitude fast activity at 15–24 c/s becomes predominant with few slower waves. The animal may just doze for a very short period, or remain awake, his heart rate may increase very slightly but his respiration is not grossly changed. For the ten times larger dose after the initial period of fast activity, larger amplitude slower waves are seen, mixed with many sharp elements and, occasionally, spikes. The animal falls into a deep sleep, the heart rate increases slightly, and respiration stops for half to one minute. Recovery takes place in 5–15 min with considerable individual variations. Only in 2 out of 17 experiments, activity characterized by a tendency to bursts and silences appeared for a few seconds following this dose.

In spite of the marked differences in the EEG changes at various ages in response to intravenous thiopentone, the clinically recognizable phenomena were similar both in the younger and in the older pups. In general, for the small dose at most ages only a very light sleep was induced, with a minor increase in heart rate and a minimal depression of respiration. For the larger dose at all ages, deep anaesthetic sleep was induced for a few minutes with an initial period of depressed respiration, or apnoea, lasting usually less than a minute, occasionally longer.

Too little is known about the many aspects of growth and development of the dog in the first three months of life to attempt any useful correlation of the three phases of evolution of cerebral response to a short-acting barbiturate with other biological events at cerebral level. These evolutional steps, however, are clear-cut and do not seem to occur at exactly the same time as other evolutional steps of the 'spontaneous' EEG in the same dogs. Meticulous studies of myelination and its phases of topological distribution might perhaps help in adding another parameter to the present observations. Further investigations with barbiturates and other drugs are necessary.

A uniform interpretation of the changes in the morphology of the electro-cardiogram could not be established because when the dog flops down, fully relaxed, there may be considerable variations in the position of the heart, which is not supported in the chest. On occasions, however, gross alterations appeared in the ECG and, as mentioned above, death may occur within a few minutes after the intravenous injection of a large dose of thiopentone, possibly due to cardio-respiratory difficulties.

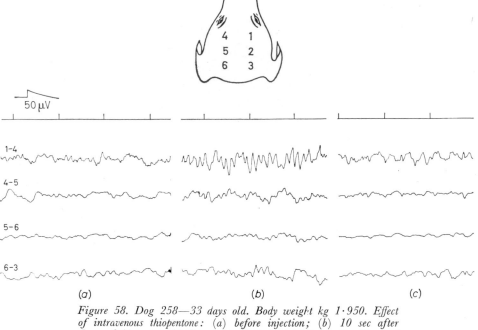

Figure 58. Dog 258—33 days old. Body weight kg 1·950. Effect of intravenous thiopentone: (a) before injection; (b) 10 sec after 5 mg of thiopentone (2·5 per cent solution); (c) 30 sec after 50 mg of thiopentone (2·5 per cent solution)

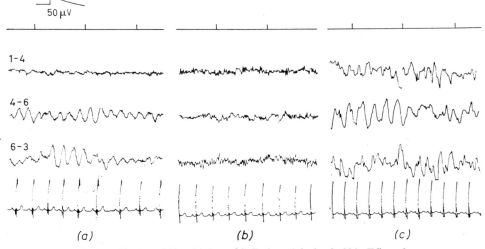

Figure 59. Dog 242—64 days old. Body weight kg 3·600. Effect of intravenous thiopentone: (a) before injection (note 5 c/s activity as vision is occluded); (b) 10 sec after 9 mg of thiopentone (2·5 per cent solution); (c) half a minute after 90 mg of thiopentone (2·5 per cent solution)

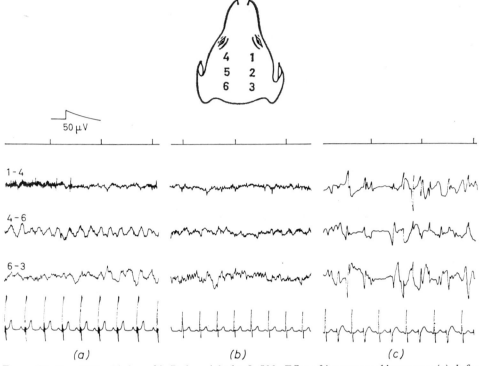

Figure 60. Dog 243—64 days old. Body weight kg 3·500. Effect of intravenous thiopentone: (a) before injection (note the rhythmic 5 c/s activity as vision is occluded); (b) 10 sec after 9 mg of thiopentone (2·5 per cent solution); (c) 1 min after 90 mg of thiopentone (2·5 per cent solution). In addition to the electrocardiographic changes there are irregular discharges in the EEG (probably not a normal response)

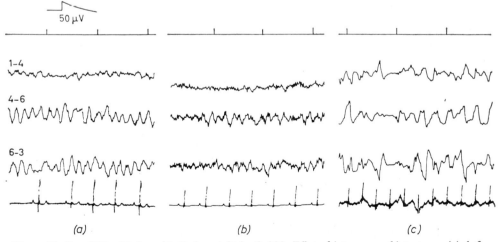

Figure 61. Dog 292—92 days old. Body weight kg 6·000. Effect of intravenous thiopentone: (a) before the injection (note the rhythmic 5 c/s activity); (b) 10 sec after 15 mg of thiopentone (2·5 per cent solution); (c) half a minute after 75 mg of thiopentone (2·5 per cent solution)

47

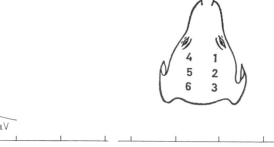

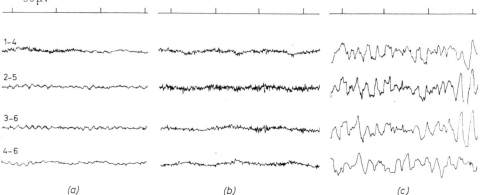

(a)   (b)   (c)

Figure 62. Dog 333—6 months old. Body weight kg 7·800. Effect of intravenous thiopentone: (a) before the injection (note the low amplitude 6–7 c/s rhythmic activity seen at this age when vision is occluded); (b) 10 sec after 19 mg of thiopentone (2·5 per cent solution) with a marked increase in fast activity; (c) 1 min after 100 mg of thiopentone (2·5 per cent solution)

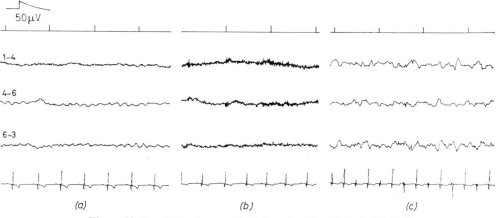

(a)   (b)   (c)

Figure 63. Dog 202—1 year old. Body weight kg 10·800. Effect of intravenous thiopentone: (a) before the injection; (b) 20 sec after 27 mg of thiopentone (2·5 per cent solution); (c) 2 min after 280 mg of thiopentone (2·5 per cent solution). The gain of the EEG was reduced to half. Note the electrocardiographic changes and the sharp elements in the EEG

Abnormal EEG Patterns (*Figures 64–75*)

This study of the normal evolution of EEG patterns in the young dog was made, not only in order to satisfy our curiosity about some aspects of normal onto-genesis, but also to recognize EEG patterns which are outside the range of 'normality' at various ages. It was often difficult to assess differences between what might be called 'unusual' or 'anomalous' patterns and the 'abnormal' ones. Because of the unknown concomitant factors following minor alterations of the testing conditions, it was difficult to assess whether transitory 'unusual' patterns might have been related to unrecognizable psychophysiological variations peculiar to particular age groups. In the absence of an expert in animal behaviour in our laboratory, many of these aspects were probably overlooked in the present study.

Future studies may show whether, in the dog, particular types of abnormal EEG patterns might be seen only when some pathological processes affect the brain at a certain age, but at present we know little about both normal and abnormal cerebral electrogenesis. A number of illustrations have been tenta-tively included in this booklet to demonstrate some of the deviations from the normal EEG patterns at various ages in relation to repeatable experimental conditions. It seems probable that particular types of EEG abnormalities might be recognizable only after a certain age, or after a particular stage of cerebral maturation is reached. For this reason, most of the examples are taken from the age of about 2 months.

Because of the large range of possible pathological features, some clinical phenomena observed in each animal of this section are mentioned, together with a brief description of the general experimental conditions which led to the 'production' of the altered cerebral condition. Further details might be found in the selected bibliography given at the end of this booklet, but much of this material is related to work still in progress in Professor B. S. Platt's M.R.C. Unit, on the effect of malnutrition upon growth and development. Although the EEG studies have been rewarding, they represent only one of the many aspects of the work of a team.

In the following illustrations only single examples of abnormal EEG patterns are included, taken from animals at an age when the abnormal features were best seen. The evolution of abnormal patterns in each animal in subsequent ages is outside the scope of this booklet.

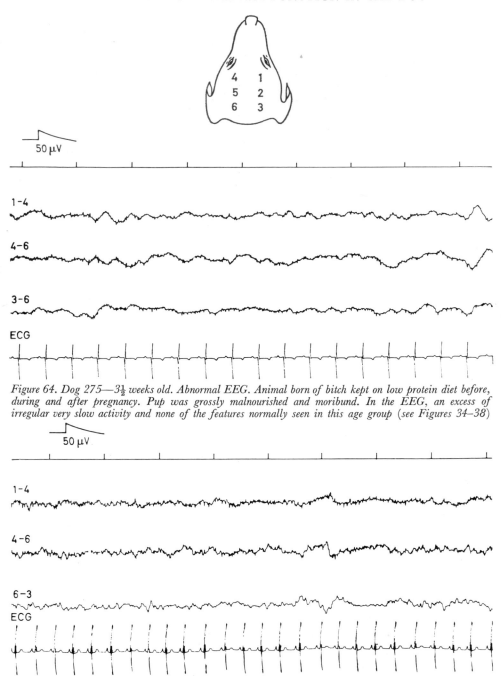

Figure 64. Dog 275—3½ weeks old. Abnormal EEG. Animal born of bitch kept on low protein diet before, during and after pregnancy. Pup was grossly malnourished and moribund. In the EEG, an excess of irregular very slow activity and none of the features normally seen in this age group (see Figures 34–38)

Figure 65. Dog 297—10 weeks old. Abnormal EEG. Animal born of bitch kept on low protein diet before, during and after pregnancy. Pup was small, malnourished, with abnormal gait and posture. In the EEG (waking state and vision occluded), an irregular activity without normal rhythmic 4–6 c/s waves seen in this age group

ABNORMAL EEG PATTERNS

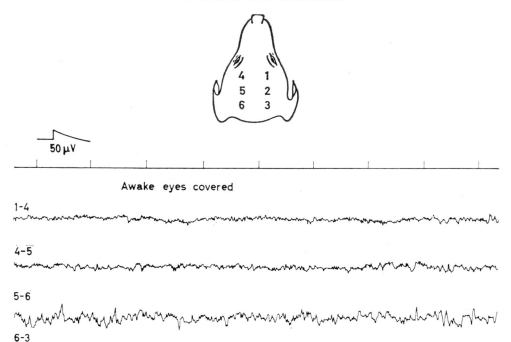

Figure 66. Dog 367—9 weeks old. Abnormal EEG. Animal born of bitch kept on low protein diet before, during and after pregnancy. Pup was undersized, malnourished, with slow gait. In the EEG (waking state, eyes covered), activity over posterior half of the brain is irregular, excessively fast with many sharp components (compare with Figures 43–47)

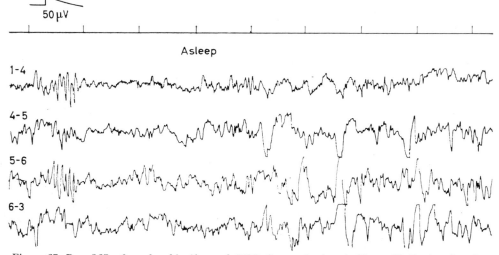

Figure 67. Dog 367—9 weeks old. Abnormal EEG. Same animal as in Figure 66. During sleep there is an excess of irregular slow activity of large amplitude mixed with many sharp elements

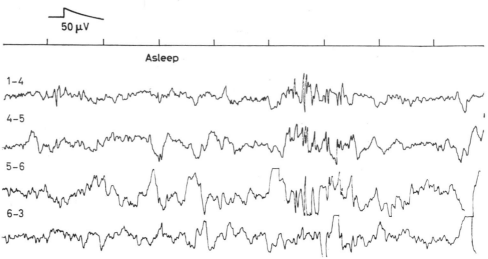

Figure 68. Dog 366—9 weeks old. Abnormal EEG. Same litter of pup 367 (Figures 66 and 67). In the EEG during sleep there is an excess of irregular slow activity of large amplitude and occasional bursts of sharp elements and spikes. No clinically recognizable seizures were seen

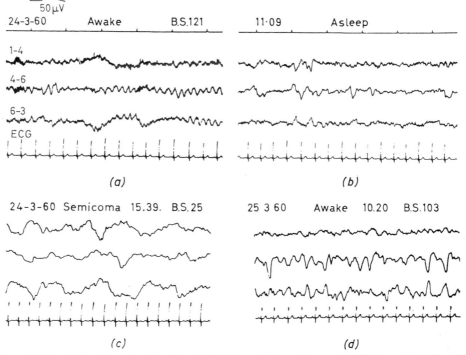

Figure 69. Dog 247—10 weeks old. Normal EEG (a and b) and abnormal EEG (c and d). The EEG was taken before, during and after insulin induced hypoglycaemia. (a) Animal awake (vision occluded) blood sugar 121 mg/100 ml; (b) spontaneous sleep a few minutes later; (c) after prolonged hypoglycaemia, two seizures, semi-comatose. Blood sugar level at this time was 25 mg/100 ml; (d) the next day animal clinically well and blood sugar level normal but in the EEG a considerable amount of slow activity persisted (awake, vision occluded)

ABNORMAL EEG PATTERNS

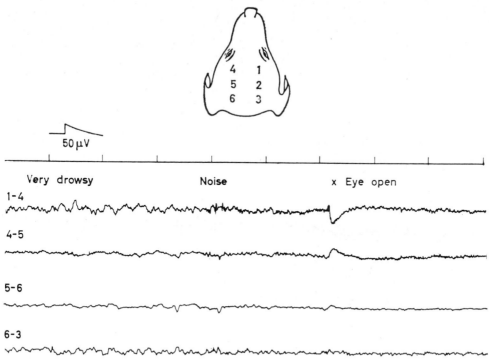

Figure 70. Dog 304—10 weeks old. Abnormal EEG. Normal animal born of normal mother no recognizable illness but remained slow and 'dopey' since administration of thiopentone when 5 weeks old (a litter mate died after a similar dose). In the EEG there is poverty of rhythmic activity, even when the animal had the eyes closed, with a poor differentiation between anterior and posterior regions of the brain (compare with normal EEG of Figures 46 and 47)

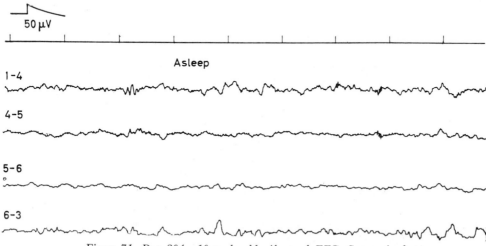

Figure 71. Dog 304—10 weeks old. Abnormal EEG. Same animal as in Figure 70. Poverty of activity during sleep (compare with normal EEG of Figures 44 and 49)

53

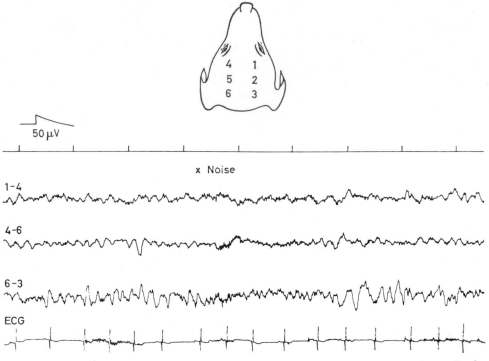

Figure 72. Dog 290—11 weeks old. Abnormal EEG. Animal kept on vitamin B_1 deficient diet but appetite still reasonably good. Early change in EEG was seen with considerable variability of dominant activity over posterior half of brain (compare with litter mate 292, on normal diet (Figures 41, 45, 48, 51))

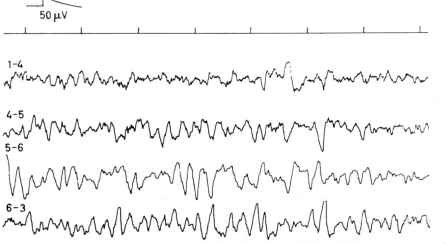

Figure 73. Dog 404—2½ months old. Abnormal EEG. Animal born after normal pregnancy. Soon after birth fed by another bitch on an abnormal diet, was underfed until weaning, and remained malnourished and grossly undersized. In the EEG, rhythmic activity is slower and more irregular than in normal litter mates (see Figures 46 and 47)

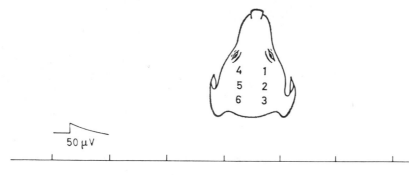

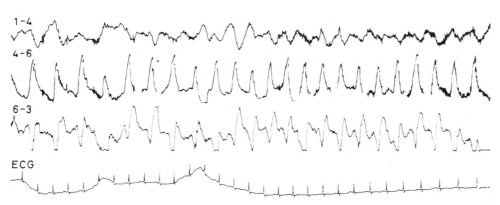

Figure 74. Dog 248—10 weeks old. Abnormal EEG. Prolonged focal discharges without recognizable clinical changes during insulin induced hypoglycaemia

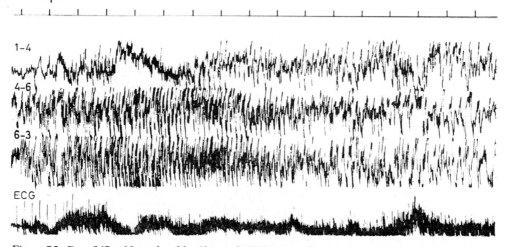

Figure 75. Dog 247—10 weeks old. Abnormal EEG. Generalized tonic and, later, clonic convulsion during insulin induced hypoglycaemia (see Figure 69)

Extracerebral Biological Electrical Phenomena (Figures 76–85)

Technical difficulties are usually met during measurements of small variations in differences of potential between regions of the scalp. Often, the traces of the electrical activity of the brain are masked by other potential changes of various nature. A few examples are given in this booklet of particular electrical phenomena of extracerebral origin peculiar to the dog at various ages. 'Artefacts' due to faults in the input, or in the recording apparatus, are not included, as these have been extensively illustrated in a number of books and atlases of EEG. The examples included are related to common extracerebral biological phenomena met during this study, superimposed upon the EEG, recorded with the method described.

Peculiar movements of the scalp, particular types of grouping of muscle action potentials, or their distribution, are often seen in the pup at some ages, and not at other ages. These phenomena might, to a certain extent, be used as an additional, though often vague, parameter of evolution of the behaviour of the animal. For example, scalp movements seen in connection with yapping, muscle action potentials of sniffing, those of shivering, of twitching, or of lifting one or both eyebrows, represent features which may give a clue as to the probable age of a normal young dog. Muscle action potentials due to orientation of the ears in response to an auditory stimulus have a different grouping and spatial distribution than those related to sniffing, to attempts to look around, or to the occasional twitch during sleep. These features are often neglected in neurophysiological and EEG studies, as their evolutional importance is overlooked.

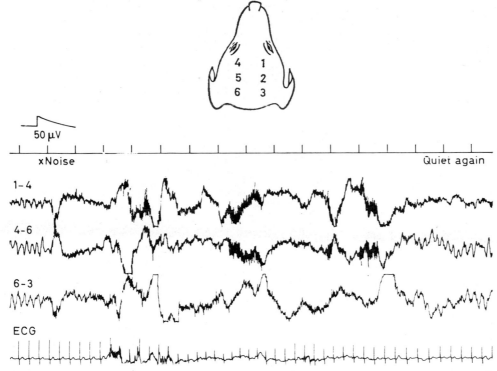

Figure 76. Dog 358—2 months old. Reduced paper speed. Following a noise, in addition to the blocking of rhythmic activity, movements of the ears, scalp and electrodes occur with corresponding potential changes. See also muscle action potentials recorded from electrodes 1 and 4 over anterior part of head while animal is raising one or both eyebrows

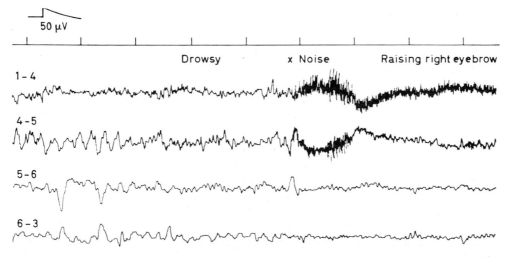

Figure 77. Dog 341—2 months old. Animal is drowsy and in response to a noise raises both eyebrows for about one second. Left eyebrow is relaxed sooner than right

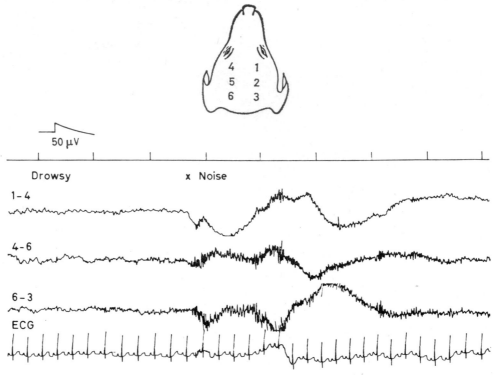

Figure 78. Dog 358—1 month old. Movements of head and scalp, as well as front paws, probably in response to a noise

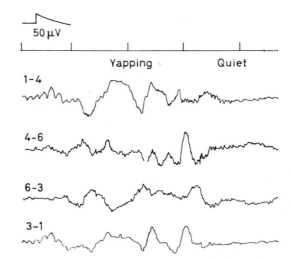

Figure 79. Dog 421—4 weeks old. Repeated movements of head and scalp while yapping

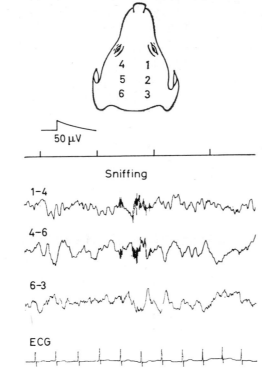

Figure 80. Dog 225—6 weeks old. Muscle action potentials while sniffing

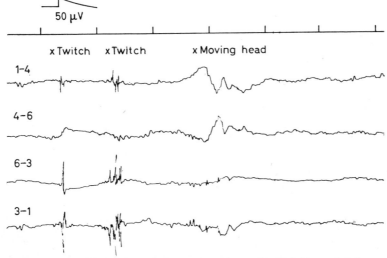

Figure 81. Dog 444—approximately 10 hours old. Twitching or brief shivering followed by slow movements of head and scalp (during probable sleep)

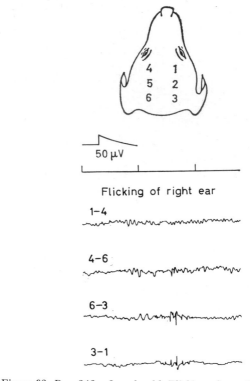

Figure 82. Dog 242—2 weeks old. Flicking of ears (right much more
than the left)

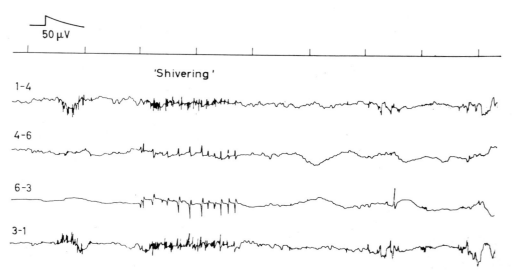

Figure 83. Dog 444—approximately 10 hours old. Prolonged
twitching or 'shivering' and isolated twitching

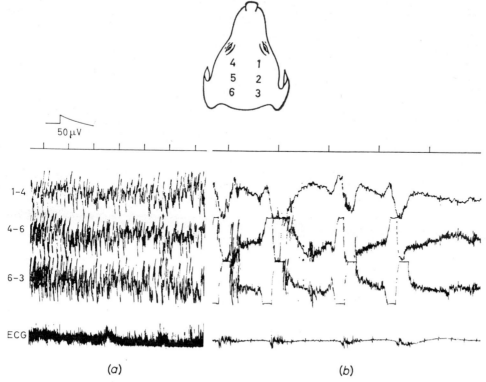

Figure 84a. Dog 247—10 weeks old. During a seizure: tonic phase
Figure 84b. Dog 247—10 weeks old. Same seizure: end of clonic phase

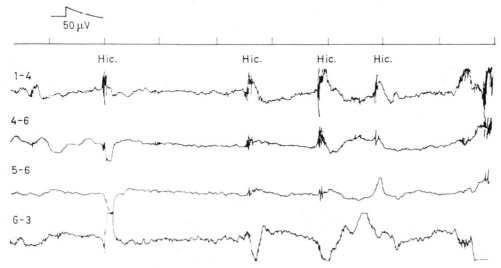

Figure 85. Dog 405—5 weeks old. Hiccough

Bibliography

As the literature on various aspects of development of cerebral function is large and widely scattered, only a selection is given below.

Adrian, E. D. (1935–36). 'The Electrical Activity of the Cortex.' *Proc. R. Soc. Med.*, **29**, 197.
— (1936). 'The Spread of Activity in the Cerebral Cortex.' *J. Physiol.*, **88**, 127.
— (1939). 'The Localization of Activity in the Brain' (Ferrier Lecture). *Proc. Roy. Soc. B***126**, 433.
— (1947). *The Physical Background of Perception*. London: Oxford University Press.
— (1947). 'General Principles of Nervous Activity.' *Brain*, **70**, 1.
— and Matthews, B. H. C. (1934). 'The Interpretation of Potential Waves in the Cortex.' *J. Physiol.*, **81**, 440.
Albertoni, P. (1881). 'Azione di alcune sostanze medicamentose sull'eccitabilità del cervello e contributo alla terapia dell'epilessia.' *Sperimentale*, **48**, 225, 337.
Amantea, G. (1912). 'Chemische Reizung der Hirnrinde des Hundes.' *Zbl. Physiol.*, **26**, 229.
— (1914). 'Effetti di compressioni circoscritte graduate sulla zona corticale sigmoidea del cane.' *Arch. Fisiol.*, **12**, 245.
— (1915). 'Sul rapporto fra centri corticali del giro sigmoideo e sensibilita cutanea nel cane.' *R.C. Accad. Lincei*, **24**, 268.
— (1922). 'Azione della stricnina e del fenolo sulle diverse zone della corteccia cerebrale del cane.' *Arch. Farmacol. sper.*, **11**, 3.
— (1926). 'Sul diverso comportamento dei cani nei riguardi dell'epilessia sperimentale.' *Boll. Soc. ital. Biol. sper.*, **1**, 1.
Anokhin, P. K. (1958). *EEG Study of Conditioned Reflexes*. Moscow.
— (1960). 'On the Specific Action of the Reticular Formation of the Cerebral Cortex.' *Electroenceph. clin. Neurophysiol.*, Suppl. 13, p. 257.
Ariëns Kappers, C. U., Huber, G. C., and Crosby, E. C. (1936). *The Comparative Anatomy of the Nervous System of Vertebrates Including Man*. New York: Macmillan.
Baglioni, S. (1900). 'Physiologische Differenzierung verschiedener Mechanismen des Rückenmarkes (Physiologische Wirkung des Strychnins und der Karbolsäure).' *Arch. Anat. Physiol., Lpz.*, Suppl. 193.
— (1916). 'The Functional Analysis of the Cortical Centres by Means of Local Chemical Stimulation.' *Quart. J. exp. Physiol.*, **10**, 169.
— and Magnini, M. (1909). 'Azione di alcune sostanze chimiche sulla zona eccitabile della corteccia cerebrale del cane.' *Arch. Fisiol.*, **6**, 240.
Beccari, N. (1943). *Neurologia comparata*. Florence: Sansoni.
Beck, A., and Cybulski, N. (1892). 'Weitere Untersuchungen über die elektrischen Ezscheinungen in der Hirnrinde der Affen und Hunde.' *Zbl. Physiol.*, **6**, 1.
Berger, H. (1932). 'Uber das EEG das Menschen', IV-V. *Arch. Psychiat. Nervenkr.*, **97**, 6; **98**, 231.
Bergland, R. M. (1960). 'Newer Concepts of Myelin Formation Correlated to Functional Changes.' *Arch. Neurol.*, **2**, 260.
Bernhard, C. G., Kaiser, I. H., and Kolmodin, G. M. (1959). 'On the Development of Cortical Activity in Fetal Sheep.' *Acta physiol., scand.*, **47**, 333.
Bishop, E. J. (1950). 'The Strychnine Spike as a Physiological Indicator of Cortical Maturity in the Post-natal Rabbit.' *Electroenceph. clin. Neurophysiol.*, **2**, 309.
Brazier, M. A. B. (1950). *Bibliography of EEG 1875-1948*. International Federation of EEG and Clinical Neurophysiology.
— (1958). 'The Development of Concepts Relating to the Electrical Activity of the Brain.' *J. nerv. ment. Dis.*, **126**, 303.
— (1960). *The Electrical Activity of the Nervous System*, 2nd ed. London: Pitman.
— (1961). *A History of the Electrical Activity of the Brain. The First Half Century*. New York: Macmillan.

BIBLIOGRAPHY

Brazier, M. A. B. (1961). *Brain and Behaviour.* Washington: American Institute of Biological Science.
— and Finesinger, J. E. (1945). 'Action of Barbiturates on the Cerebral Cortex.' *Arch. Neurol. Psychiat., Chicago,* **53**, 51.
Bremer, F. (1935). 'Cerveau isolé et physiologie du sommeil.' *C.R. Soc. Biol., Paris,* **118**, 1235.
— (1938). *L'Activité Electrique de l'Ecorce Cérébrale.* Paris: Hermann.
— (1953). *Some Problems in Neurophysiology.* University of London Athlone Press.
Brizzee, K. R., and Jacobs, L. A. (1959). 'Postnatal Changes in Volumetric and Density Relationships of Neurons in Cerebral Cortex of Cat.' *Acta Anat.,* **38**, 291.
Brody, S. (1947). *Bioenergetics and Growth.* New York: Reinhold.
Brožek, J. (1962). 'Soviet Studies on Nutrition and Higher Nervous Activities.' *Ann. N.Y. Acad. Sci.,* **93**, 665.
Bures, J. (1957). 'The Ontogenetic Development of Steady Potential Differences in the Cerebral Cortex in Animals.' *Electroenceph. clin. Neurophysiol.,* **9**, 121.
Burns, B. D. (1958). *The Mammalian Cortex.* London: Arnold.
Busacca, A., and Rizzolo, A. (1926). 'L'azione dei glucosidi sulla corteccia cerebrale.' *Ann. clin. Ter.,* **6**, 161.
Buser, P., and Borenstein, P. (1956). 'Réponses corticales secondaires à la stimulation sensorielle chez le Chat curarisé non anesthésié.' *Electroenceph. clin. Neurophysiol.,* Suppl. 6, pp. 89-108.
— — and Bruner, J. (1959). 'Etude des systèmes associatifs visuels et auditifs chez le Chat anesthésié au chloralose.' *Electroenceph. clin. Neurophysiol.,* **11**, 305.
Bykov, K. M. (1959). *The Cerebral Cortex and the Internal Organs.* Moscow: Foreign Languages Publishing House.
Cadilhac, J., Passouant-Fontaine, T., and Passouant, P. (1962). 'L'organization des divers stades du sommeil chez le chaton de la naissance à 45 jours.' *J. Physiol. (Paris),* **54**, 305.
Cajal, S. Ramon y (1909–11). *Histologie du Système Nerveux de l'Homme et des Vertébrés.* Paris: Maloine.
Calvet, J., and Scherrer, J. (1961). 'Activité bioélectrique de l'écorce cérébrale à ses différents niveaux.' *C.R. Soc. Biol., Paris,* **155**, 275.
Cammermeyer, Jan (1961). 'Frequency of Meningoencephalitis and Hydrocephalus in Dog.' *J. Neuropath.,* **20**, 386.
Caton, R. (1875). 'The Electric Currents of the Brain.' *Brit. med. J.,* **2**, 278.
— (1887). 'Researches on Electrical Phenomena of Cerebral Grey Matter.' *IX. Internat. Med. Congress. 1897. Sect. Physiology,* vol. 3, p. 246.
Caveness, W. F. (1962). *Atlas of EEG in the Developing Monkey (Macaca mulatta).* London: Pergamon.
Charles, Margaret S., and Fuller, John L. (1956). 'Developmental Study of the EEG of the Dog.' *Electroenceph. clin. Neurophysiol.,* **8**, 645.
Clementi, A. (1929). 'Stricininizzazione della sfera corticale visiva ed epilessia sperimentale da stimoli luminosi.' *Arch. Fisiol.,* **27**, 356.
— (1935). 'Sfera gustativa della corteccia cerebrale del cane ed epilessia sperimentale riflessa a tipo sensoriale gustativo.' *Boll. Soc. ital. Biol. sper.,* **10**, 902.
Conel, J. Le R. (1939-1959). *The Postnatal Development of the Human Cerebral Cortex,* I-VI. Cambridge, Mass.: Harvard University Press.
Davis, H., Davis, P. A., Loomis, A. L., Harvey, E. N., and Hobart, G. (1939). 'Electrical Reactions of the Human Brain to Auditory Stimulation during Sleep.' *J. Neurophysiol.,* **2**, 500.
De'Finis, M. L. (1931–32). 'Effetti della iperventilazione polmonare sull'attività della zone sensitivo-motrice corticale del cane.' *Arch. Fisiol.,* **30**, 494.
Dodgson, M. C. H. (1962). *The Growing Brain (an Essay in Developmental Neurology).* Bristol: Wright.
Döllken (1898). 'Die Reifung der Leitungsbahnen im Thiergehirn.' *Neurol. Zbl.,* **17**, 996.
Dreyfus Brisac, C. (1957). 'Activité électrique cérébrale du foetus et du très jeune prématuré.' *Rapports 1er Congrès intern. Sciences Neurol. Bruxelles,* p. 163.
— and Blanc, C. (1956). 'EEG et maturation cérébrale.' *Encephale,* **45**, 205.
— Flescher, J., and Plassart, E. (1962). 'L'EEG: critère d'âge conceptionnel du nouveau-né à terme et prématuré.' *Biol. Neonat.,* **4**, 154.

Dusser de Barenne, J. G., Garol, H. W., and McCulloch, W. S. (1951). 'Functional Organization of Sensory and Adjacent Cortex of the Monkey.' *J. Neurophysiol.*, **4**, 324.

— and McCulloch, W. S. (1938). 'Functional Organization in the Sensory Cortex of the Monkey (Macaca mulatta).' *J. Neurophysiol.*, **1**, 69.

Eccles, J. C. (1953). *The Neurophysiological Basis of Mind.* Oxford: Clarendon Press.

Ellingson, R. J. (1958). 'EEG of Normal, Full-term Newborns Immediately after Birth with Observations on Arousal and Visual Evoked Responses.' *Electroenceph. clin. Neurophysiol.*, **10**, 31.

— and Lindsley, D. B. (1949). 'Brain Waves and Cortical Development in Newborns and Young Infants.' *Amer. Psychologist*, **4**, 248.

— and Wilcott, R. C. (1960). 'Development of Evoked Responses in Visual and Auditory Cortices of Kittens.' *J. Neurophysiol.*, **23**, 363.

Ferrier, D. (1876). *Functions of the Brain.* London.

Fessard, A. (1957). *Bases physiologiques et aspects cliniques de l'Epilepsie.* Paris: Masson.

Field, J., Magoun, H. W., and Hall, V. E. (eds) (1959). *Handbook of Physiology—Section of Neurophysiology.* Washington: American Physiological Society.

Fischgold, H., and Gastaut, H. (eds) (1957). *Conditionnement et Réactivité en EEG.* Paris: Masson.

Flexner, L. E., Tyler, D. B., and Gallant, L. J. (1950). 'Biochemical and Physiological Differentiation in Developing Cerebral Cortex of Foetal Guinea-pig.' *J. Neurophysiol.*, **13**, 427.

Follis, R. H., Jr. (1958). *Deficiency Disease.* Springfield, Ill.: Thomas.

Frauchiger, E. (1945). *Seelische Erkrankunzen bei Mensch und Tier.* Bern: Huber.

Fuller, J. L., Easler, C. A., and Banks, E. M. (1950). 'Formation of Conditioned Avoidance Responses in Young Puppies.' *Amer. J. Physiol.*, **160**, 462.

Fulton, J. F. (1949). *Physiology of the Nervous System.* Oxford University Press.

Garcia-Austt, E. (1957). 'Ontogenic Evolution of the Electroencephalogram in Human and Animals.' *Rapports* 1er *Congrès intern. Sciences Neurol. Bruxelles*, pp. 173-7.

Gellhorn, E., and Kessler, M. (1942). 'The Effect of Hypoglycaemia on the EEG at Varying Degrees of Oxygenation of the Blood.' *Amer. J. Physiol.*, **136**, 1.

Gerard, R. W., and Libet, B. (1939). 'The Control of Normal and "Convulsive" Brain Potentials.' *Amer. J. Psychol.*, **19**, 1125.

Gibbs, F. A., and Gibbs, E. L. (1950). *Atlas of Electroencephalography*, 2nd ed. Massachusetts: Addison-Wesley Press.

Gliozzi, S. M. (1927). 'Sull'epilessia sperimentale da eccitamenti afferenti nel gatto.' *Arch. Fisiol.*, **25**, 749.

Goldensohn, E. S., Busse, E. W., Spencer, J. N., Draper, W. B., and Whitehead, R. W. (1950). Studies on Diffusion Respiration—VII: The Cortical Electrical Activity of Dogs.' *Electroenceph. clin. Neurophysiol.*, **2**, 33.

Gozzano, M. (1941). 'L'elettroencefalografia.' *Arch. Psicol. Neur. Psich.*, **2**, 413.

Granit, R. (1955). *Receptors and Sensory Perception.* Newhaven: Yale University Press.

Grossman, C. (1955). 'Electro-ontogenesis of Cerebral Activity.' *A.M.A. Arch. Neurol. Psychiat.*, **74**, 186.

— (1957). 'Topic Ontogenic Evolution of the Electroencephalogram in Human and Animals.' *Discussion. Rapports* 1er *Congrès. Int. Sciences neurol., Bruxelles*, pp. 157-62.

Gurevich, B. C. (1954). 'Recording of EEG in Chronic Experiments with Dogs.' *J. Physiol. USSR.*, **40**, 484.

Hafez, E. S. E. (ed.) (1962). *The Behaviour of Domestic Animals.* London: Baillière Tindall & Cox.

Harlow, H. F., and Woolsey, C. N. (1958). *Biological and Biochemical Bases of Behaviour.* University of Wisconsin Press.

Heard, C. R. C., Meyer, A., Pampiglione, G., Stewart, R. J. C., and Platt, B. S. (1961). 'Clinical, EEG, and Pathological Changes in the Nervous System of Experimental Animals.' *Proc. Nutr. Soc.*, **20**, 1.

Henry, C. E. (1944). 'EEG of Normal Children.' *Monogr. Soc. Res. Child Developm.*, **9**, No. 39.

Hernandez-Peon, R. (1960). 'Neurophysiological Correlates of Habituation.' *Electroenceph. clin. Neurophysiol.*, Suppl. 13, pp. 101-14.

Hill, J. D. N., and Parr, G. (eds.) (1950). *Electroencephalography.* London: Macdonald.

BIBLIOGRAPHY

Himwich, H. E. (1951). *Brain Metabolism and Cerebral Disorders*. Baltimore: Williams and Wilkins.

Himwich, W. A., and Petersen, J. C. (1959). 'Correlation of Chemical Maturation of the Brain in Various Species with Neurologic Behaviour.' In *Biological Psychiatry*, pp. 1-16. J. Masserman (ed.), New York: Grune and Stratton.

Hoagland, H. (1940). 'A Simple Method for Recording Electrocorticograms in Animals Without Opening the Skull.' *Science*, **92**, 537.

Hunt, W. E., and Goldring, S. (1951). 'Maturation of Evoked Response of the Visual Cortex in the Postnatal Rabbit.' *Electroenceph. clin. Neurophysiol.*, **3**, 465.

Jacobs, J., and Snider, R. S. (1949). 'Developmental Relationships Between Electrical Activity and Histogenesis of the Cerebellum.' *Fed. Proc.*, **8**, 80.

Jasper, H. H. (1937). 'Electrical Signs of Cortical Activity.' *Psychol. Bull.*, **34**, 7, 411.

Jouvet, J. (1962). 'Recherches sur les structures nerveuses et les mechanismes responsables des differentes phases du sommeil.' *Arch. Ital. Biol.*, **100**, 125.

Jouvet, M., and Hernandez-Peon, R. (1957). 'Mechanismes neurophysiologiques concernant l'habituation, l'attention et le conditionnement.' *Electroenceph. clin. Neurophysiol.*, Suppl. 6, pp. 39-49.

Jung, R. (1939). 'Das Elektroncephalogramm und seine klinische Anwendung (I. Methodik der Ableitung, Registrierung und Deutung des EEG).' *Nervenarzt*, **12**, 569.

— (1949). 'Hirnelektrische Untersuchungen uber den Elektrogram: die Erregungsableite in corticalen und subcorticalen Hirnregionen bei Katze und Hund.' *Arch. Psychiat. Nervenkr.*, **183**, 206.

Kellaway, P. (1957). 'Ontogenic Evolution of the Electrical Activity of the Brain in Man and in Animals.' *Rapports* 1er *Congrès intern. Sciences neurol. Bruxelles*, pp. 141-54.

Kennard, M. A., and Nims, L. F. (1942). 'Changes in the Normal EEG of Macaca Mulatta with Growth.' *J. Neurophysiol.*, **5**, 325.

Kleitman, N. (1939). *Sleep and Wakefulness*. Chicago University Press.

Knott, J. R., and Gibbs, F. A. (1939). 'A Fourier Transform of the EEG from 1 to 8 Years.' *Psychol. Bull.*, **36**, 512.

Kogan, A. B. (1960). 'The Manifestations of Processes of Higher Nervous Activity.' *Electroenceph. clin. Neurophysiol.*, Suppl. 13, pp. 51-64.

Konorski, J. (1948). *Conditioned Reflexes and Neuron Organization*. London: Cambridge University Press.

Koppanyi, T., and Dille, M. (1935). 'Remarks on the Distribution of Barbiturates in the Brain.' *J. Pharmacol.*, **54**, 84.

Kornmueller, A. E. (1932). 'Architektonische Lokalisation bioelektrischer Erscheinungen auf der Grosshirnrinde. Untersuchungen am Kanichen bei Augenbelichtung.' *J. Psychol. Neurol., Lpz.*, **44**, 447.

Koupernik, C. (1954). *Développement psycho-moteur du premier âge*. Presses Université de France.

Lapras, M. (1959). 'Epilepsie Spontanée du Chien.' *Thèse Doct. Veter. Université Lyon*.

Leontovich, T. A., and Mering, T. A. (1956). 'Craniocerebral Topography of the Dog.' *Biull. Eksp. Biol. Med. (Moskva)*, 42, **71**.

Libet, B., Fazekas, J. F., and Himwich, H. E. (1941). 'The Electrical Response of the Kitten and Adult Cat Brain to Cerebral Anemia and Analeptics.' *Amer. J. Physiol.*, **132**, 232.

— and Gerard, R. W. (1941). 'Steady Potentials Fields and Neurones Activity.' *J. Neurophysiol.*, **4**, 438.

Lim, R. K. S., Liu, C. N., and Moffitt, R. L. (1960). *A Stereotactic Atlas of the Dog's Brain*. Springfield, Ill.: Thomas.

Lindsley, D. (1936). 'Brain Potentials in Children and Adults.' *Science*, **84**, 354.

— (1939). 'A Longitudinal Study of the Occipital Alpha Rhythm in Normal Children.' *J. Genet. Psychol.*, **55**, 197.

Livanov, M. N. (1940). 'Rhythmic Stimulation and Interrelations between Various Cortical Areas.' *J. Physiol. USSR*, **28**, 172.

— (1960). 'Concerning the Establishment of Temporary Connections.' *Electroenceph. clin. Neurophysiol.*, Suppl. 13, pp. 185-98.

Loeb, C. (1951). 'Corpo calloso e commessura anteriore nella trasmissione interemisferica dell' "afterdischarge" nel cane.' *Sist. Nerv.*, **5**, 339.

65

Loeb, C. and Sacchi, U. (1952). 'Sulla produzione di emboli per via carotidea nel cane.' *Sist. Nerv.*, **3**, 186.

Luciani, L., and Tamburini, A. (1878 and 1879). 'Ricerche sperimentali sulle funzioni del cervello.' *Riv. sper. Freniat.*, **4**, 69, 225; **5**, 1.

Lurie, R. N., and Trofimov, L. G. (1956). 'EEG Recording from Different Areas of the Cerebral Cortex of a Dog in a Chronic Experiment.' *J. Physiol. USSR*, **42**, 348.

McGrath, J. T. (1953). 'Neurological Examination of the Dog with some Clinicopathological Observations.' *Vet. Ext. Quart. Univ. Pa.*, No. 132 (ref. in *Vet. Rec.*, **66**, 348).

McGraw, M. B. (1943). *The Neuromuscular Maturation of the Human Infant.* New York: Columbia University Press.

Magoun, H. W. (1958). *The Waking Brain.* Springfield, Ill.: Thomas.

Marinesco, G., Sager, O., and Kreindler, A. (1936). 'Etudes électroencéphalographiques. Électroencéphalogramme du Chat et de Cobaye nouveau-nés.' *Bull. Acad. nat. Med. (Paris)*, **115**, 873.

Marty, R. (1962). 'Développement post-natal des réponses sensorielles du cortex cérébral chez le chat et le lapin.' *Thèse (Faculté des Sciences) Université de Paris.* Paris: Masson.

— (1962). 'Aspects évolutifs des activités sensitivo-sensorielles au cours du développment.' *J. Physiol. (Paris)*, **54**, 373.

— Contamin, F., and Scherrer, J. (1959). 'La double réponse électrocorticale à la stimulation lumineuse chez le Chat nouveau-né.' *C.R. Soc. Biol., Paris*, **153**, 198.

Melin, K. A. (1953). 'The Development of the Electrical Activity of the Brain and its Changes under Pathological Conditions.' *Schweiz. Arch. Neurol. Psychiat.*, **71**, 217.

Menzel, R., and Menzel, R. (1937). 'Welpe und Umwelt.' *Kleintier u. Pelzt.*, **13**, 1.

Meyer, A., Pampiglione, G., Platt, B. S., and Stewart, R. J. C. (1961). 'Neurological, EEG and Neuropathological Changes in Dogs with Experimental Malnutrition.' *VII Internat. Congr. of Neurol.*, etc. *Rome 1961. Excerpta Med. Internat. Congr. Series, No. 39*, p. 15.

Monti, F. (1956). 'La semiologia del sistema nervoso negli Animali domestici.' *Veterinaria Ital.*, Suppl. 7.

Morgan, L. O., and Johnson, C. A. (1930). 'Experimental Lesions in the Tuber Cinereum of the Dog Followed by Epileptiform Convulsions and Changes in Blood Chemistry.' *Arch. Neurol. Psychiat., Chicago*, **24**, 696.

Moruzzi, G. (1939). 'Etude de l'Activite Electrique de l'Ecorce Cerebrale dans l'Hypo-glycémie Insulinique et dans Differéntes Conditions Modifiant le Métabolisme des Centres.' *Arch. int. Physiol.*, **48**, 45.

— (1943). 'Contributi alla fisiologia generale dei centri nervosi. I: Azione dell'anemia acuta sull'attivita dei neuroni encefalici, inibitori ed eccitatori.' *Arch. Fisiol.*, **43**, 1.

— (1946). *L'epilessia sperimentale.* Bologna: Zanichelli.

Mourek, J. (1959). 'Oxygen Consumption during Ontogenesis in Rats in Environment with a High and Low Oxygen Content.' *Physiol. Bohemoslov.*, **8**, 106.

Pampiglione, G. (1952). 'Induced Fast Activity in the EEG as an Aid in the Location of Cerebral Lesions.' *Electroenceph. clin. Neurophysiol.*, **4**, 79.

— (1953). 'Some Observations on the Variability of Evoked EEG Activity.' *Electroenceph. clin. Neurophysiol.*, **5**, 123.

— (1954). 'Short Acting Barbiturates During Direct Recording from the Human Brain.' *Electroenceph. clin. Neurophysiol.*, **6**, 346.

— (1960). 'The Development of the EEG in the Young Dog.' *Electroenceph. clin. Neurophysiol.*, **12**, 760.

— (1961). 'Alertness and Sleep in Young Pigs.' *Electroenceph. clin. Neurophysiol.*, **13**, 827.

— (1962). 'Demonstration of a Technique for Recording EEG in Young Animals and Man.' *J. Physiol.*, **162**, 10P.

— (1961). 'The Development of Some Rhythmic Activity in the Electroencephalogram of the Young Dog.' *J. Physiol.*, **159**, 27.

— and Ackner, B. (1958). 'The Effect of Repeated Stimuli upon EEG and Vasomotor Activity during Sleep in Man.' *Brain*, **81**, 1, 64.

— Stewart, R. J. C., and Platt, B. S. (1960). 'Electroencephalographic and Electrocardio-graphic Techniques in Nutritional Studies on Laboratory Animals.' *Proc. Nutr. Soc.*, **19**, ix.

BIBLIOGRAPHY

Pampiglione, G., Friend, C. J., and Heard, C. R. C. (1962). 'Electroencephalographic Observations during Induced Hypoglycaemia in Young Dogs and Pigs.' *Proc. Nutr. Soc.*, **21**, i.

Papez, J. W. (1929). *Comparative Neurology*. New York: Crowell.

Pavlov, I. P. (1927). *Conditioned Reflexes*. Oxford University Press.

Peters, J. J., Vonderahe, R., and Huesman, A. A. (1960). 'Chronological Development of Electrical Activity in the Optic Lobes, Cerebellum and Cerebrum of the Chick Embryo.' *Physiol. Zöol.*, **33**, 225.

Platt, B. S. (1961). 'Malnutrition and the Central Nervous System.' In *Chemical Pathology of the Nervous System*. London: Pergamon.

Práwdicz-Neminski, W. W. (1925). 'Zur Kenntnis der elektrischen und Innervationsvorgänge in den funktionellen Elementen und Geweben des tierischen Organismus. Elektro-cerebrogramm der Säugetiere.' *Pflüg. Arch. ges. Physiol.*, **209**, 362.

Prosser, C. L., and Brown, F. A. (1961). *Comparative Animal Physiology*. Philadelphia: Saunders.

Pupilli, G. C. (1949). 'L'attivitè elettrica continua defli aggregati neurronici.' *Atti III Congr. Soc. Ital. Fisiol.*, 3-5 Oct.

Purpura, D. P. (1956). 'Observations on the Cortical Mechanisms of EEG Activation Accompanying Behavioural Arousal.' *Science*, **123**, 804.

Radouco-Thomas, C., Martin, F., Chaumontet, J. M., and Royo, D. (1960). 'Electro-ontogenèse, comportement et R.C. pendant la maturation cérébrale du rat.' *Proc. 2nd Meeting. C.I. Neuropsychopharmacologicum, Basle.*

Ramirez De Arellano, M. I. R. (1961). 'Maturational Changes in the Electroencephalogram of Normal Monkeys.' *Exp. Neurol.*, **3**, 209.

Rheinberger, M. B., and Jasper, H. H. (1937). 'Electrical Activity of the Cerebral Cortex in the Unanaesthetized Cat.' *Amer. J. Physiol.*, **119**, 186.

Roger, A., Sokolov, E., and Voronine, L. (1957). 'Le conditionnement moteur à l'état de veille et pendant le sommeil.' *Rev. Neurol.*, **96**, 460.

Roitbak, A. I. (1960). 'Electrical Phenomena in the Cerebral Cortex during the Extinction of Orientation and Conditioned Reflexes.' *Electroenceph. clin. Neurophysiol.*, Suppl. 13, pp. 91-100.

Rossi, G. (1912). 'Ricerche sulla eccitabilità della corteccia cerebrale in cani sottoposti ad emiestirpazione cerebellare.' *Arch. Fisiol.*, **10**, 251.

Rossi, G. F., and Zirondoli, A. (1955). 'On the Mechanism of the Cortical Desynchronization Elicited by Volatile Anaesthetics.' *Electroenceph. clin. Neurophysiol.*, **7**, 383.

Ruckebusch, Y. (1963). 'Etude de l'évolution post-natale due sommeil physiologique chez l'agneau.' *Arch. Ital. Biol.* **101**, 111.

— (1963). 'L'EEG normal du chien.' *Rev. Med. Vet.*, **114**, 119.

Rusinov, V. S., and Rabinovitch, M. Y. (1958). 'EEG Researches in the Laboratories and Clinics of the Soviet Union.' *Electroenceph. clin. Neurophysiol.*, Suppl. 8.

Sakhiulina, G. T. (1951). 'Methods for Recording Cerebral Potentials in Chronic Dogs.' *J. Higher Nervous Activity (USSR)*, **1**, 457.

— (1955). 'Modifications in the EEG of Dogs During the Formation and Consolidation of a Conditioned Reflex.' *Proc. Acad. Sci. USSR*, **104**, 153.

— (1960). 'EEG of Dogs in Some Complex Forms of Conditioned Reflex Activity.' *Electroenceph. clin. Neurophysiol.*, Suppl. 13, pp. 211-20.

Samson-Dollfus, D. (1955). *L'EEG du Prématuré jusqu'à l'Age de 3 Mois, et du Nouveau-né à Terme.* Paris: Foulon.

Scherrer, J., and Oeconomos, D. (1954). 'Réponses corticales somesthétiques du mammifère nouveau-né.' *Etudes neonotales*, **3**, 199.

— Contamin, F., and Verley, R. (1960). 'Maturation comparée des réponses électrocorticales et des activités motrices et neuro-végétatives chez les Mammifères (Primates exceptés).' *Rapports 1er Congès Europ. Pedo psychiatrie, Paris*, pp. 61-76.

Schlottauer, C. F. (1948). 'Nervous Ailments of Dogs.' *J. Amer. vet. med. Ass.*, **112**, 48.

Scott, J. P., and Marston, M. V. (1950). 'Critical Periods Affecting the Development of Normal and Maladjustive Social Behaviour of Puppies.' *J. genet. Psychol.*, **77**, 25.

Sechenov, I. (1962). *Selected Physiological and Psychological Works*. Moscow: Foreign Languages Publication House.

Sherrington, C. S. (1947). *The Integrative Action of the Nervous System*. Cambridge University Press.

Smith, J. R. (1938). 'The EEG during Normal Infancy and Childhood (I-III).' *J. genet. Psychol.*, **53**, 431, 455, 471.

Sobotka, P. (ed.) (1960). 'Functional and Metabolic Development of the Central Nervous System.' *International Symposium Plzeň (Czechoslovakia)*.

Swank, R. L., and Watson, C. W. (1949). 'Effect of Barbiturates and Ether on Spontaneous Electrical Activities of Dog Brain.' *J. Neurophysiol.*, **12**, 137.

Tanner, J. (1962). *Growth at Adolescence*, 2nd ed. Oxford: Blackwell Scientific Publications.

Tilney, F., and Casamajor, L. (1924). 'Myelinogeny as Applied to the Study of Behavior.' *Arch. Neurol. Psychiat., Chicago*, **12**, 1.

Tuge, H., Kanayama, Y., and Chang, H. Y. (1960). 'Comparative Studies on the Development of EEG.' *Jap. J. Physiol.*, **10**, 211.

Turner, O. A. (1948). 'Growth and Development of the Cerebral Cortical Pattern in Man.' *A.M.A. Arch. Neurol. Psychiatry*, **59**, 1.

Tyler, D. B. (1940-41). 'The Mechanism of the Production of Brain Damage during Insulin Shock.' *Amer. J. Physiol.*, **131**, 554.

— and Van Harreveld, A. (1942). 'The Respiration of the Developing Brain.' *Amer. J. Physiol.*, **136**, 600.

— Goodman, J., and Rothman, T. (1947). 'The Effect of Experimental Insomnia on the Rate of Potential Changes in the Brain.' *Amer. J. Physiol.*, **149**, 185.

Van Harreveld, A., Tyler, D. B., and Wiersma, C. A. G. (1943). 'Brain Metabolism during Electro-narcosis.' *Amer. J. Physiol.*, **139**, 171.

Venturoli, M. (1962). 'L'EEG Normale del Cane.' *Clin. Veterinaria*, **85**, 525.

Verley, R. (1959). 'Développement des activités électrocorticales, motrices et neurovégétatives des Mammifères nouveau-nés.' *Thèse Medecine, Paris*.

— (1961). 'Activités électrocorticales du Chat et de Lapin nouveau-nés sous curare.' *J. Physiol., Paris*, **53**, 493.

Voronin, L. G., and Sokolov, E. N. (1960). 'Cortical Mechanisms of the Orienting Reflex and its Relation to the Conditioned Reflex.' *Electroenceph. clin. Neurophysiol.*, Suppl. 13, pp. 335-46.

Waelsch, H. (ed.) (1955). *Biochemistry of the Developing Nervous System*. New York: Academic Press.

Walter, W. G. (1950). 'The Functions of the Electrical Rhythms in the Brain.' *J. ment. Sci.*, **96**, 1.

— (1950). 'The Principles and Methods of Location.' *Electroenceph. clin. Neurophysiol.*, Suppl. 2, pp. 9-15.

— (1953). *The Living Brain*. London: Duckworth.

Werner, J. (1960). 'Concerning the Ontogenesis of Brain Potentials in the Spontaneous EEGs of New Born Dogs.' *Electroenceph. clin. Neurophysiol.*, **12**, 256.

Windle, W. F., Fish, M. W., and O'Donnell, J. E. (1934). 'Myelogeny of the Cat as Related to Development of Fiber Tracts and Prenatal Behaviour Patterns.' *J. comp. Neurol.*, **59**, 139.

Winkelman, N. W., and Moore, M. T. (1940). 'Neurohistopathologic Changes with Metrazol and Insulin Shock Therapy.' *Arch. Neurol. Psychiat., Chicago*, **43**, 1108.

Wolstenholme, G. E. W., and O'Connor, C. (eds) (1958). *Neurological Basis of Behaviour* (Ciba Foundation Symposium). London: Churchill.

Woolsey, C. N. (1952). 'Patterns of Localization in Sensory and Motor Areas of the Cerebral Cortex.' In *The Biology of Mental Health*. New York: Hoeber.

Yoshii, N., and Tsukiyama, K. (1951). 'Normal EEG and its Development in the White Rat.' *Jap. J. Physiol.*, **2**, 34.

Zagami, V. (1930). 'Contributi alla conoscenza dell'azione dell'insulina, con particolare riguardo alla sindrome ipoglicemica.' *Arch. Fisiol.*, **28**, 339.